How It Is
Nowadays

THEODORE CLYMER · PRISCILLA HOLTON NEFF

CONSULTANTS

ROGER W. SHUY · E. PAUL TORRANCE

LINGUISTICS CREATIVITY

GINN AND COMPANY
A XEROX COMPANY

Acknowledgments

Grateful acknowledgment is made to the following authors and publishers for permission to use and adapt copyrighted materials:

Frank Bonham, for his story "A Pet Named Jet."

Ruth V. Bortin, for her poem "Cotton Candy Country."

Clyde Robert Bulla, for his story "The Invitation."

Julia W. Cunningham, for her poem "Just for You."

Sid Fleischman, for his story "Let's Make Up a Story."

Don Freeman, for his story "The Scooter."

Harper & Row, Publishers, for permission to reprint the poem "Rudolph Is Tired of the City" from *Bronzeville Boys and Girls* by Gwendolyn Brooks, Copyright ⓒ 1956 by Gwendolyn Brooks Blakely.

McGraw-Hill Book Company for the poem "Valentine for Earth" from *The Little Naturalist* by Frances Frost. Copyright ⓒ 1959 by Estate of Frances Frost and Kurt Werth. Used with permission of McGraw-Hill Book Company.

David McKay Company, Inc., for "The Donkey Egg," adapted, and reprinted by permission of David McKay Company, Inc., from *Once the Hodja* by Alice Geer Kelsey. Copyright 1943 by Alice Geer Kelsey.

Harriette H. Miller, for her stories "Flossie Flamingo" and "William's Wish," for her play "The Three Spinning Fairies," and for her poem "Christopher, the Contrary Chameleon."

Katherine Q. Morton, for her story "Special Visitors."

G. P. Putnam's Sons for the poem "Cookout Night" by Dorothy Aldis. Copyright ⓒ 1964 by Dorothy Aldis. Reprinted by permission of G. P. Putnam's Sons from *Is Anybody Hungry?* by Dorothy Aldis.

Cynthia Stone Richmond, for her story "Dippy's Day by Moonlight."

Charles Scribner's Sons, for the poem "Like a Bug" by Aileen Fisher. Reprinted with the permission of Charles Scribner's Sons from *Cricket in a Thicket* by Aileen Fisher. Copyright ⓒ 1963 Aileen Fisher; and for the poem "Where Go the Boats?" from *A Child's Garden of Verses* by Robert Louis Stevenson, published by Charles Scribner's Sons.

Dorothy S. Thomas, for her story "The Handre."

Nancy Byrd Turner, for her poem "Good-Night Song."

Helen K. Warfel, for her story "Kukui and the Golden Cat."

Charlotte Zolotow, for her story "The Farmer's Hut."

Acknowledgment for helpful advice is made to the following scientists: Dr. Tom Helliwell, Dr. Jon Mathews, Dr. Samuel Neff, and Dr. John S. Shelton.

ILLUSTRATORS: Don Albright, Ray Ameijide, Willi Baum, James Bowen, Ray Cruz, Bernard D'Andrea, Lorraine Fox, Sue Gernes, Trina Hyman, Susan Jeffers, David Kelley, Allan Mardon, John Martucci, Tonia Noell, Joan Paley, Arthur and Pauline Perry, Jerry Pinckney, Angela Sciaraffa, George Suyeoka, Dianne Winer, Hans Zander.

Contents

4

COTTON CANDY COUNTRY

In Cotton Candy Country,
  Which isn't far away—
Your work's all done before you start,
  There's only time for play.
Stars are twinkling ice-cream cones
  And lollipops are growing,
And music from the carousels
  On every breeze is blowing.

8

There are trains that cross the country
    That are tidy as can be.
They never leave their tracks sprawled out
    For everyone to see.
They take you where you want to go,
    But always, you will find,
Spread out their rails in front of them
    And roll them up behind.
There are golden palominos
    And pinto horses too,
Who, if you ask politely,
    Will gladly carry you
Like thistledown upon a breeze,
    Swift as a falling star,
Just because they like you—
    But it's rude to ride too far.

The loveliest sight you see there,
  If you have the luck to go,
Is the magic dance of butterflies
  When the new moon is aglow.
A million fireflies light the scene
  While crickets play the tune.
The colors shine and glimmer so
  The lazy little moon
Comes sliding half-way down the sky
  To see the pretty sight—
Thirty-thousand butterflies
  Dancing all the night.

Ruth V. Bortin

10

KuKui and the Golden Cat

Kukui was a mynah bird, and Pineapple was a golden cat. They lived in a house high on a hill on the island of Maui with the woman who owned them. The mynah bird and the golden cat did not trust each other.

Kukui lived in a cage. He was safe from Pineapple's claws but he could not help himself to her food. That was in the cat's own dish on the floor.

11

Kukui was a bird of many tricks and he was a real mimic. Pineapple was safe from the bird's long sharp beak, but she was never free from the noise of his talk.

"Yeh-heh, yeh-heh, yeh-heh," he shouted when Pineapple was having a cat nap and their mistress was not there.

Sometimes Kukui made his voice mimic the voice of their mistress. This always gave Pineapple a mixed-up feeling.

12

"Here pussy, nice pussy, come and get your food, Pineapple," Kukui would call in his mistress' sweet voice. He kept calling all day long.

Because she was so sure of that voice, Pineapple would come running to her food dish, but often she found nothing there.

If Pineapple came too close to Kukui's cage, the bird had another way to trick the cat. "Help, HELP!" he would mimic in his mistress' voice. Whenever he yelled long enough, Mistress was sure to come running.

13

One afternoon, as soon as the sun dipped into the sea, Kukui knew that it was almost time for Pineapple's supper. So he called softly, "Here pussy, nice pussy, come and get your food, Pineapple."

At the sound of her mistress' voice, the golden cat came faster than ever for the food which was not there.

When Pineapple found the dish with nothing in it, she knew Kukui was playing another trick. Her tail rose. But she could not stop the mynah bird's noise. "Yeh-heh, yeh-heh, yeh-heh," Kukui yelled over and over again.

14

Another fine afternoon when the rains were over, and the sun had begun to shine, Mistress set Kukui's cage on the wide garden wall behind the house.

For a long time Kukui preened himself and pointed his beak toward the sky.

"Hele pēlā, hele pēlā!" he yelled. That means, "Go away, go away!"

The sun moved toward the sea. Shadows were on the hills. A quiet came over the mountain. Kukui's loud noise stopped.

He gave a sharp look around. On a bank on the other side of the wall, a long gray mongoose was quietly creeping. His nose was pointed toward Kukui's cage.

Suddenly, like a shadow, the mongoose was on the wall behind the cage. Then he was moving around it. Closer and closer he moved, trying to get at the mynah bird.

Kukui yelled every call he knew. He was so upset that he called, "Here pussy, nice pussy, come and get your food!"

"Yeh-heh, yeh-heh, yeh-heh," coaxed Kukui. "Hele mai, hele mai." That means, "Come here, come here."

Suddenly Pineapple came running. She leaped to the wall behind the mongoose and moved toward the animal's tail.

But as Pineapple was about to jump, the mongoose suddenly turned and bit the golden cat.

Kukui yelled and yelled. "Help, HELP!" He pointed his beak toward the cat.

A house door banged, and Mistress came running. All this noise was too much for the mongoose. He quickly ran back into the shadows, and Mistress took her pets back into the house.

It took many weeks for Pineapple to get well again, but Kukui never stopped trying to help her. Day after day the golden cat took cat naps while Kukui chanted, "Nice pussy, nice pussy."

And every afternoon Pineapple was sure that food was in her dish when the mynah bird called, "Here pussy, nice pussy, come and get your food, Pineapple."

17

THE FARMER'S HUT

Once there was a farmer.

He lived in one room of his small hut
with his wife and her mother
and his three small children.

He worked hard on his farm all day.
When he came home at night,
the noises in his house drove him crazy.

His wife talked to him.
His mother-in-law talked to him.
His three small children talked to him.
And they all talked at the same time!

The poor farmer put his hands
over his ears and cried,
"Please, please, QUIET, please!"
But they went right
on talking.

At last, in desperation,
he asked the advice of a wise man.

"What shall I do?" he asked.
"The noise is driving me crazy!"

"Will you follow my advice?"
the wise man asked.

"Yes," said the farmer.

"Good," the wise man said.
"Go home and bring
one cow into the house with you."

"A cow in the house!"
cried the farmer.
"How could that help?"

"Well, if you don't want my
advice . . . ," the wise man said.

19

So the farmer went home
and brought the cow into his house.

"A cow in the house!" said his wife.

"A cow in the house!"
said his mother-in-law.

"A cow in the house!"
said the children.

And they all said it at once.

"Moooooooo," said the cow,
bewildered by the noise.

The poor man just held his head.

"Quiet, please, QUIET, all of you!"
he cried.

20

The next day he went back
to the wise man.

"Well," said the wise man,
"how is it?"

"Worse than ever,"
said the farmer.

"While they talk,
the cow moos.
It's terrible!"

"Good," said the wise man.
"You have a dog?"

"Yes," said the farmer,
"two of them."

"Good," said the wise man.
"Tonight bring the dogs
into the house too."

"Bring the dogs into the house!"
shouted the farmer.

"Well—if you don't want
my advice . . . ," said the wise man.

So the farmer went home
and brought the two dogs into the house too.

"A cow and two dogs!" said his wife.

"A cow and two dogs in the house!"
said his mother-in-law.

"A cow and two dogs in the house!"
said the children.

"Moooooooo," said the bewildered cow.

And the two dogs barked
at being locked up inside.

The poor farmer just held his head.

"Quiet, please, all of you,"
he moaned.

The next day the farmer went back
to the wise man.

"How is it now?" the wise man asked.

"Worse, worse than ever," said the farmer.
"Are you sure you know what you are doing?"

"Yes," said the wise man.
"Tonight I want you to be sure to
bring indoors your rooster and all the hens."

"My rooster and all the hens!"
cried the farmer. "How will that help?"

"Well—if you don't want
my advice . . . ," the wise man said.

23

So the farmer went home
and brought his rooster and
all the hens into his house.

"A cow, two dogs, a rooster
and all these hens in the house!"
said his wife. "Are you crazy?"

"A cow, two dogs, a rooster
and all these hens!" said his
mother-in-law. "Are you crazy?"

"A cow, two dogs, a rooster,
and all our hens!" cried the children.

"Moooooooo . . ," went the cow.

"Werf werf werf," went the dogs.

"Cackledecackle decackle," went
the hens while the rooster crowed.

"Quiet," moaned the poor man.
"Oh, quiet."

24

The next day the farmer went back to the wise man.

"How is it?" the wise man asked.

"Terrible," said the farmer,
"terrible. I cannot last another night like this."

"All right," said the wise man.
"Now listen with care. Tonight,
go home and be sure to put the cow
back in the barn."

The farmer did, and while there
was still a lot of noise, at least the
cow was not there to moo at him.

The following night
he went to the wise man again.

"How was it?" the wise man asked.

"Better," the farmer said,
"better than the night before."

"Good," the wise man said.
"Tonight go back and be sure to put out
the two dogs."

And that night there was a lot
of noise. But at least there was
no cow mooing and no dogs barking.
"How was it?" the wise man
asked the next night:
"Better," the man said.
"Fine," the wise man said.
"Tonight go home and put out
the rooster and the hens."
And the farmer did.
No cow mooed at him.
No dogs barked.
No rooster crowed.
No hens cackled.
It was wonderful!

Next night he went back
to the wise man.

"How is it now?" the wise man asked.

"Last night it was wonderful," the farmer
said, "so quiet, so quiet,

no mooing

no barking

no crowing

no cackling.

IT'S WONDERFUL—JUST WONDERFUL

"Good," said the wise man,
"I told you it would be better."
And the farmer went home.
His wife and mother-in-law
and three children said,
"At last, you have come
to your senses again."
But he only smiled to himself.
For without the cow
and the two dogs
and the rooster
and the hens
their voices seemed very quiet indeed.

INDEED!

Flossie Flamingo

Flossie Flamingo flew back to Florida to spend the winter. Right away she knew things had changed. Not far from the marsh where she lived, a huge, round, pointed thing jutted into the air.

Flossie said to her friend, Olive Owl, who knew everything, "How things have changed around here! What is that big tall thing?"

"It's a rocket," said Olive.

"It looks like a big silo," said Flossie. "I once stayed near a farm with a silo. Are you sure it isn't a silo?"

"Yes, I'm sure," said Olive Owl. "I flew over and listened to the men talking when they were building it. They said it was a rocket. They said it was going to—"

"It's a rocket-silo," Flossie decided. "Yes, I'm sure that's what it is." And home she went.

Day after day Flossie Flamingo flew past the rocket-silo. After a while she saw it so often she hardly noticed it.

Then early one morning, she did notice smoke at the base of the rocket-silo.

"Where there's smoke there's fire!" she cried.

Sure enough, red flames shot out with a roar.

"The rocket-silo is burning up!" yelled Flossie Flamingo, but it was so early that no one heard her.

Flossie could hardly believe her eyes. Slowly at first, and then faster and faster, the rocket-silo was lifted into the air. Trailing smoke and fire, it roared out of sight, leaving Flossie's ears ringing.

"How terrible! The rocket-silo has torn a great hole in the sky," cried Flossie. "Who would believe it! Soon all the stars will fall through! I must find a safe place to hide."

She flapped over to an old log. Standing on one foot, she tucked her head under her wing and shut her eyes.

Soon her friend, Hilda Heron, flew by the old log and noticed Flossie.

"Why, Flossie Flamingo," said Hilda. "Why are you asleep so early in the day?"

"I'm not asleep," said Flossie, lifting her wing a little and looking out from under it. "Everything's changed around here. I'm hiding, and you'd better hide too! The rocket-silo tore a great big hole in the sky, and all the stars are going to fall out."

"How terrible!" said Hilda Heron. "How did you find out about it?"

"I saw it! I heard it!" cried Flossie. "Quick! Find a safe place."

So Hilda Heron crouched beside Flossie Flamingo and put her head under her wing.

In a little while Katy Crane flew by and saw Flossie and Hilda.

"What are you doing down there?" she called as she floated down for a landing.

"We're hiding," said Hilda Heron. "And you'd better hide too. Have you noticed the sky? The rocket-silo tore a big hole in it and all the stars are going to fall out."

"How terrible!" said Katy Crane. "How did you find out about it?"

"Flossie Flamingo told me," said Hilda.

"Yes, yes," said Flossie. "Early this morning I saw it! I heard it! Hurry! Find yourself a safe place."

So Katy Crane got very close to Hilda Heron and put her head under her wing.

34

A little later Rachel Rail flew by. She saw Flossie and Hilda and Katy, and she landed with a thud.

"Are you having a party?" asked Rachel.

"No," said Katy Crane. "We're hiding and you'd better hide too. The rocket-silo tore a great hole in the sky, and any time now all the stars will come falling through."

"How terrible!" said Rachel Rail. "How did you find out about it?"

"Hilda Heron told me," said Katy Crane.

"Flossie told me," said Hilda Heron.

"Yes, yes," said Flossie Flamingo, poking her bill out from under her wing. "I saw it! I heard it! Hurry! Find a safe place."

35

So Rachel Rail crowded close beside Katy Crane, and there the four of them stayed for the rest of the day.

Then after it was dark, Olive Owl came flying by looking for her dinner.

"How strange!" she said when she saw the four birds crouched side by side on the log. "What are you doing here after dark?"

"We're hiding," said Rachel Rail, "and you'd better hide too."

"For goodness sake, why?" asked Olive Owl.

"There's going to be a terrible change," added Katy Crane. "Any second now all the stars will fall through. You'd better believe it!"

"How did you find out about all this?"
asked Olive Owl.

"Flossie Flamingo told us," said Hilda.

"Yes, yes," said Flossie in a hushed voice
from under her wing. "I saw it! I heard it!
Quick! Find a safe place."

"My tree is safe enough for me," said
Olive Owl. "But right now I'm going to find
some dinner."

"What? What?" said the others. "Aren't you
going to hide? What about the rocket-silo?"

"I don't know about a rocket-silo," said
Olive Owl. "But I do know a rocket left for
the moon early this morning. I watched it
go."

"But the hole in the sky!" said Flossie Flamingo.

"Open your eyes and look," said Olive Owl.

Slowly they all took their heads from under their wings and looked up. There were the stars, all in their same places. Nothing had changed.

"Oh," said Flossie Flamingo. "I guess the stars aren't going to fall after all."

"I guess not," said the others.

"I guess not!" said Olive Owl.

Cookout Night

Paper cups and paper plates.

Pickles in a pickle jar.

Popcorn in a crackly bag.

Salt and pepper?

Here they are.

Paper napkins! Who forgot?

"I didn't, you did."

"I did *not*.

Besides, what difference does it make?

Look at all the grass around

For wiping hands and faces on . . ."

Nothing's ever impolite:

Not outdoors on cookout night.

Dorothy Aldis

39

William's Wish

BIRTHDAY CANDLES

It was William's birthday. He was having a party with his family and six of his best friends. Because his birthday was in August, and the weather was nice and warm, the party was in William's backyard. There were games of "Balloon Tag" and "Peanut Hunt," and there were hot dogs and slices of ice-cold watermelon to eat. After that, William opened his gifts. Last of all, when it was almost dark, Mother brought out a big cake with seven candles.

"Make a wish, William," said Dad.

"You have to blow out all the candles at once," said his friend Mark.

"That's right," said Mother. "If you do, you'll get your wish before your next birthday."

"Take a deep breath," said Miss Brooks, who lived next door.

"Close your eyes," said William's sister Julie.

William took a deep breath and closed his eyes.

"Now BLOW!" said everyone all at once.

William blew, and out went every one of the candles.

"Good for you," said Mother. "Now you'll get your wish."

"I hope so," said William, "because I wished—"

"Don't tell!" interrupted Julie. "If you tell, your wish won't come true."

"That's right," Miss Brooks agreed.

"I won't tell," said William. "But how long do I wait for my wish to come true? Till it's time for another birthday party?"

"It could be soon," Miss Brooks said.

"Or take a whole year," suggested Julie.

William sighed. "A whole year. That's fall, winter, spring, and summer again. A whole year is a long time to wait for a wish."

For the rest of the summer and the first part of fall William waited, and he didn't tell his wish. Then school started. It was fun to walk home with Mark and cross the busy highway at the corner.

One fall afternoon William and Mark were waiting for the light to turn green, when they saw a big truck with a load of hay. William saw Mark close his eyes, lick his thumb, and pound his right fist into his left hand.

"What're you doing?" asked William.

"Making a wish," said Mark. "Everyone knows that's how you wish on a load of hay."

"I didn't know it," said William. "I could have been making a wish too."

"Not on that load of hay, because—"

"Why not?" interrupted William.

"You have to wish as soon as you see it. If you talk first, it's no good. And you can't look back."

"Does it work?" asked William. "I mean, does your wish really come true?"

"I never kept track," said Mark. "Come on. The light's changed to green."

That night William told Julie about making a wish on a load of hay.

"It would have been fun to try it," he said. "And my birthday wish may really come true faster if I keep making the wish."

"You could make a new wish," suggested Julie.

"A new wish?" William thought about it. Then he sighed, "I don't think I'll make a new wish till I get my birthday wish."

"Why not?" asked Julie.

"Well, today Mark said he never kept track of his wishes. Did you ever keep track?"

"No, not really," said Julie.

"Well, I think I'll just keep wishing that same birthday wish. That way I'll know."

45

It was nearly a week before William saw a load of hay, but he remembered to lick his thumb and pound his left hand with his right fist. Then he took a deep breath and wished his birthday wish. He didn't look back.

All that fall William waited, but he didn't tell his wish. He wished again when he and Julie snapped the Thanksgiving turkey wishbone. William got the long end of it, but when winter came, his wish still hadn't come true.

46

STARS AND EYELASHES

One clear winter evening William went out to get the newspaper. It wasn't quite dark but already he could see one bright star. William looked hard at the star and chanted softly,

"Star light, star bright,
First star I've seen tonight,
I wish I may, I wish I might
Have the wish I wish tonight."

Once again he wished his birthday wish.

Back inside he gave Dad the paper and said, "I just wished on the evening star."

"Where did you hear of that?"

"I don't know," said William. "I guess everyone knows about wishing on a star."

Julie looked up from her homework. "You can wish on shooting stars too," she said. "Only you don't see them often."

"I've never seen one," sighed William, "but I'll look for them from now on."

All through the winter William looked for shooting stars, and he waited, and he didn't tell his birthday wish. One day he learned about wishing on a white horse. By spring William had wished on three white horses, but hadn't seen one shooting star, and his wish hadn't come true.

Then one bright windy afternoon
William opened the front door
and called, "Hi, Mom! I'm home
from school!"

"Already?" said Mom giving him a
hug. Then she stopped, really looked
at his face, and said, "Hold still,
you've got an eyelash."

"I've got a whole bunch of them."

"I know, but this one's loose. Here. Get
it on your hand and you can make a wish.
It might come true," said his mother.

"On an eyelash? I never heard of that."

"You close your eyes, and wish, and blow.
If your eyelash is gone, you know it went
to make your wish come true."

49

"Do wishes really come true, Mom?"

"Some people say they do," Mom answered.

"I never get my wishes," William said with a sigh. "I've already wished that same wish over and over. I'm tired of wishing it."

William looked at the eyelash on his hand, closed his eyes, wished his birthday wish, and blew as hard as he could. When he looked, the eyelash was gone.

"If that eyelash really went to get my wish," he said, "I sure hope it hurries!"

A few weeks later Miss Brooks showed him how to wish on the first robin of spring, but when spring was over, William's wish still hadn't come true.

DO WISHES COME TRUE?

Then summer came. On the Fourth of July William's family went to the fireworks show at the park. They sat for a long, long time waiting for it to get dark, but when the first bright skyrocket burst in the air William forgot the long wait. Every "firework" lit the sky in a shower of shooting stars. William wasn't sure they were the right kind of shooting stars, but he wished and wished.

The next day Mom said, "We're finally getting some warm July weather. Let's eat outdoors tonight."

That evening, after William had finished his second hot dog and his third slice of watermelon, he sat down on the lawn. Julie sat beside him and picked a dandelion stem with a fuzzy ball at the end.

"Here," she said. "You can blow on this and make a wish."

"No, thanks," said William.

"You shouldn't give up just because you didn't get your birthday wish," said Julie.

"I'm not giving up," said William. "I finally got my wish."

"You did ?"

"Sure. I got it tonight. I wished we'd eat outdoors and have hot dogs and watermelon, and tonight we did," William said.

"You mean that's what you've been wishing for nearly a year ?" asked Julie.

William nodded.

"Well, didn't your wish come true?"

"Sure," said William. "But maybe all my wishes didn't matter. I don't think I really believe in wishes."

"I don't, either. I just half-believe," said Julie, as she went to get more watermelon.

It wasn't quite dark, but just over the back fence William could see one bright star in the clear July sky. Softly he began to chant,

"Star light, star bright . . .

I wish I may, I wish I might . . ."

Tell How You Feel

Read each paragraph on this page. Pretend you are the farmer or the cat or the owl. Be ready to tell how you feel.

1. A farmer lived in one room of a small hut with his wife, their three small children, and his wife's mother. When he came home at night, the noises in his house drove him crazy. He put his hands over his ears and cried, "Please, please, *quiet*, please!" He went to a wise man for advice.

> Pretend you are the farmer. How does all this noise make you feel? Tell the wise man all about it.

2. Pineapple was a cat. Kukui was a mynah bird in a cage. Kukui could mimic their mistress' voice. Many times Kukui called Pineapple to come for his food when the food was not there.

> You are Pineapple. You are tired of being fooled. Tell your mistress all about it.

3. Olive Owl saw the flamingo, the rail, the heron, and the crane all hiding. They told Olive that there was a hole in the sky and that the owl should hide too.

> You are the owl. You think your friends are very silly. Tell another owl friend about them.

How Many Parts in a Story?

Most stories have a beginning, a middle, and an end. At the beginning of the story you meet the animals or persons and learn about their problem. In the middle of the story, exciting things happen as the characters try to find a way to solve the problem. The last part of the story usually tells how the problem is solved.

Think about "The Farmer's Hut." Who was the main character and what was his problem? What happened as he tried to solve it? How did the story end?

One of the pictures below tells about a main character and her problem. Can you find this picture?

Another picture tells about the most exciting part of a story. Can you find it? Find the picture that shows how one of the stories ends.

Hexagons and Words

On this page are two hexagons. Count the number of sides and you can guess what a hexagon is. In the middle of each hexagon is an ending to a word. In the outside parts of the hexagon are letters for you to put with the letters in the center to make a word. Read the sentences at the side, look at the hexagon, and make the word that the sentence tells about.

1. It is something good to eat.
2. It is in something that you write with.
3. You need to use this all the time.
4. If you are afraid, you do this.
5. A heavy step can be called one.
6. Something that is not alive is this.

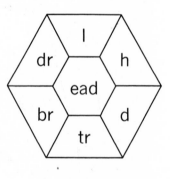

1. Dogs that do not like each other do this.
2. This is the opposite of left.
3. Something that is not loose is this.
4. The sun is this on some days.
5. You have this if you can see.
6. An airplane trip is called this.

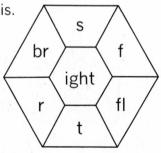

56

Finding a Way

SPECK

Spring was coming to Tait Primary School. On the new highway big trucks went by the school all day. And new red, green, and yellow signals were ready at the school crossing. The girls and boys in Miss Day's class were talking about them.

"I'm sure you know how to obey the new signals, don't you?" Miss Day asked.

Mark Zapella answered. "First we check the lights. Green, red, or yellow. We know about them. But now we watch for the new signal that says W-A-L-K. Then we obey it and go across the highway, and we stay inside the crosswalk lines."

Everyone nodded but Ben. He was thinking about his dog, Speck.

Ann Dines added something. "My mother meets me every day after school. She doesn't want me to cross the highway without her."

"Why not?" Mark asked. "All we have to do is obey the new signals."

The children talked and Miss Day listened. Finally she asked Ben a question, "What do you think about obeying signals?"

Ben said, "I was thinking about my dog, Speck. He obeys."

Speck was Ben's new Springer Spaniel. His coat was black with white specks in it. He could do tricks. He could catch a ball. He could stand on his hind legs and beg. He knew how to obey signals.

"How many signals can Speck obey?" Miss Day asked.

Ben named them. "When my Dad says 'Come,' Speck comes. When Dad says 'Heel,' Speck walks along beside him. He says 'Stay!' and Speck stays where he is until Dad tells him to move. Oh, Speck obeys signals all right."

Ann asked another question, "Does he obey you?"

"Yes," Ben said. "I'm his master now, and he's just learned how to fetch."

"How does he fetch?" asked Ann.

"Well, my baby sister creeps everywhere now. Sometimes she goes too far away. I call Speck and point to the baby. I say 'Fetch!' and Speck races to her. He pulls at her dress with his teeth. He doesn't tear her dress. He never bites her. He just pulls her back to me. Then I give him a special biscuit. That special biscuit makes him happy and . . ."

Mark Zapella interrupted, "Can you bring Speck to school so we can see him fetch?"

Ben said, "I can't bring my baby sister too, but I could bring her doll and show you. That's how I trained Speck. He learned to fetch with the doll."

"May I bring my little sister to watch Speck?" Ann Dines asked. "Little Jenny needs to learn to obey too."

Ben did bring Speck to school one afternoon, and Ann brought Little Jenny for this special time.

Speck obeyed every command that Ben gave him.

"Fetch!" Ben commanded. He pointed to the doll. All the children watched Speck, especially Jenny.

62

Speck skidded across the schoolroom floor to the doll. He clamped his teeth into her dress. With great care he pulled her back to his master.

Jenny laughed and laughed.

After school Ben took Speck out to the school crosswalk near the new signals. His father was going to meet them there.

"Sit!" Ben commanded, and Speck obeyed. He sat very upright, close to his master's feet. Ben watched the highway for his father's truck. It was time for it to come.

Ann Dines came out with Jenny to wait for their mother.

"Sit, stay, fetch!" Jenny commanded Speck, but the dog did not move.

Ben wished the truck would come. Jenny was a pest.

Then Ben heard a horn. His father's truck was moving slowly toward the crosswalk.

64

Jenny began to jump up and down. "Over there! Over there! There's Mommy!"

Across the highway at the other end of the crosswalk Mrs. Dines was waiting. The signal light was red, and Jenny's mother was signaling her to wait with Ann.

The truck was rolling closer. Jenny did not notice the truck or the red light or her mother's signaling. Before Ann could stop her, Jenny darted out into the crosswalk.

Ben saw her. He bent down and pointed to Jenny. "FETCH HER!" he commanded.

In one bound Speck had Jenny by her dress. He gave a quick hard pull, and Jenny landed on the curb again. She was screaming, but she was safe.

The truck had stopped. The brakes had been strong enough to hold. Ben's father jumped out of the truck and hurried over to the children.

Ann helped Jenny stand up, and she put her arms around her little sister. Jenny stopped screaming and watched Ben and Speck.

Ben was patting Speck. "Good dog, good dog," he kept saying as he pulled out a special biscuit. "Sit!" he ordered. "Stay!" Speck obeyed the commands, and Ben gave him the biscuit.

Now the crosswalk signal said W-A-L-K. Mrs. Dines hurried across the highway. "Oh, Jenny!" she cried. "That dog saved you."

Speck just sat upright beside his master and chewed his biscuit.

Roady-Roadrunner And Yoshi

Roady-Roadrunner lived in the high desert. His house was a prickly bush by the side of the road. Yoshi lived in the high desert too. Every morning on her way to school Yoshi passed Roady's house, and he always ran out of the bush to greet her.

Roady had strong legs for running, and a long strong tail. The tail stayed out straight behind him when he ran. When he stopped running, his tail would stand straight up. It was like a brake. It helped Roady to make a quick stop.

67

One morning when Roady ran to meet Yoshi, he sang a strange song. It sounded a little like a cuckoo, because Roady belonged to the cuckoo family. He sang the song, and then he cocked his head.

Yoshi stood and looked at him. "If I could run as fast as you run," she said, "I could be on time for school. I am late every day."

Roady ran ahead of Yoshi and made a quick stop at a fork in the road. He braked his run with his strong tail. Then he stood there, waiting for Yoshi.

At the fork one road went on in a straight line to the school. It was the best way to go. It was the shorter way.

Yoshi did not go the shorter way. On that road a big black dog lived. He barked at her. He was very strong, and one day he had pushed her down. She was afraid of him.

The other road was longer. Yoshi went that way to school. She hurried. Sometimes she ran. But she was always late for school because that way took longer.

Her teacher, Mr. Pine, always looked upset when she came in late. Today he said, "Yoshi, you are late again! Please promise to be on time tomorrow. Why is it that you are always late?"

Yoshi stood with her head down and could not answer. If she told about the dog, the children would laugh at her.

At closing time Mr. Pine said, "Promise to be on time tomorrow, Yoshi. Please try."

"I will try," she said softly. "I promise."

The next morning Roady-Roadrunner did not run out to meet Yoshi. She heard a whirring buz-z-z-z in the bush. It sounded like a rattlesnake.

Yoshi looked behind the bush. There was Roady, and there was a small rattlesnake. It was ready to strike Roady!

But Roady did not run away on his strong fast legs. He ran straight at the little snake. The snake missed its strike, and Roady pecked at its head. Then Roady jumped back and stopped where the snake could not strike him. He was ready to run at it again.

Roady was in danger. He was a brown bird, all alone. He did not run away, but the snake did. It found a rock and crawled under it.

Yoshi ran back to the road, but Roady was there first. He cocked his head and gave her his greeting.

Yoshi bowed. "You are a brave bird," she said. "You are really strong."

Then she started to go on to school.

Roady ran ahead to the fork of the road. He braked his tail and looked at her and sang his cooing song.

"Are you telling me not to be afraid?" Yoshi asked the bird as she came to the place where the road forked.

She looked down the shorter road to the school and saw the dog lying there. She looked at Roady and remembered how bravely he had faced the snake.

Yoshi took a big breath. "I can look after myself too," she said. And she took the shorter way.

She walked right by the dog. It growled a little, but she did not stop. The dog did not bark. It did not get up.

"I guess you know me this time," Yoshi said. She walked straight ahead to school. Mr. Pine smiled when he saw her. "You remembered your promise. You're on time!"

Yoshi looked straight at Mr. Pine. She said, "Roady-Roadrunner helped me."

Aquí Está Mi Nieta

Ana Rosa had come to stay with her grandmother in the United States and go to school there. On the first morning Grandmother walked to school with Ana Rosa. They were speaking in Spanish. At school Ana Rosa would speak English and learn some new words.

"You will find new friends here, Ana Rosa," her grandmother said. "They will help you with the new English words."

Ana Rosa nodded. She was looking at the tall flagpole in front of the school. Two boys were raising the flag.

Her grandmother called to one of them, "Eduardo, aquí está mi nieta !"

Eduardo ran to meet them. He spoke to Ana Rosa in English. "Hi! Let's go to our room. Everyone wants to see you!"

To her grandmother he said, "I'll show her the way home after school." And he led Ana Rosa to the classroom.

The teacher said, "Welcome, Ana Rosa." "Why don't you sit at Eduardo's table?" she suggested. "Then he can help you."

"Thank you," said Ana Rosa.

Everyone was smiling at her. These new friends were giving her a good welcome.

"Oh," she thought as she listened to the new sounds,

"it's easy

to understand."

Just before closing time the teacher said, "Let's go out to the playground to show Ana Rosa what we know about our shadows."

"Let's show her where her shadow is when the afternoon sun is behind her in the west," someone suggested.

"I'll trace her shadow on a long sheet of paper," Eduardo said.

Ana Rosa did not know the English word "shadow," so she did not understand the talk. And why was everyone going outdoors?

At a sunny spot on the sidewalk Eduardo said, "Turn your back to the sun, Ana Rosa." He pointed in the right direction.

He unrolled the paper on the walk in front of her feet. With a big black marker he traced the outline of her shadow. It was almost as long as the sheet of paper.

The children pointed in the direction of the sun. "There's the sun behind you in the west. Your shadow's in front of you. What does that tell you, Ana Rosa?" they asked.

Ana Rosa did not understand. The teacher tried to help her. "The sun is in the west in the afternoon, Ana Rosa. Your shadow helps to show you where the west is."

But no one helped Ana Rosa with the new English word "shadow." It was like being lost and not finding the way.

Eduardo understood. "Never mind," he suggested softly to her in Spanish. "On our way home your shadow will be in front of you. That's all you need to remember."

The school bell rang, and it was time to go home.

"Meet me at the flagpole," Eduardo said.

Ana Rosa said good-by to her new friends and walked to the flagpole.

The flag was gone, and so was Eduardo. Where was he? How could she find her way home? She stood on the front walk and waited. She looked in all directions. Everything looked strange.

She looked down at the sidewalk. Her own black shadow was in front of her feet. It was like finding a friend.

"My shadow," Ana Rosa said in Spanish. She said it again in English. And this time she remembered Eduardo's words.

Could the shadow lead her in the right direction ? Could it lead Ana Rosa back to her grandmother's house ?

Ana Rosa took a step forward. The shadow moved forward too. The sun was behind her. She walked on, finding a way while her shadow stayed in front of her. She let the shadow lead her until she heard Eduardo's voice behind her, calling, "Ana Rosa, wait for me !"

When he reached her, he pointed to a house just ahead of them. "There's your grandmother's house," he said. "You knew how to find your way alone, didn't you ?"

"With my shadow to show me," Ana Rosa said, "it was easy !"

The Mystery of the Suitcase

Mrs. Emory lived in a little house. Her kitchen door looked out on tall trees. In the summer the kitchen door stood wide open.

Charles Workman lived in a big two-story house nearby. The Workman family were new in the neighborhood. Charles and Mrs. Emory had become good friends. He liked to sit on the steps outside her door and watch her make cookies.

Day after day Mrs. Emory made cookies in her kitchen. No one in the neighborhood knew why. Those cookies were a mystery. But Charles did know what kind of cookies they were.

On Monday Mrs. Emory always made gingersnaps. Monday was a spicy day.

On Tuesday she baked brownies. The air around the kitchen was pretty sweet on Tuesday.

The next day she made peanut-butter cookies. Charles Workman liked these best.

Thursday cookies were never the same.

"Thursday is my leftover day," Mrs. Emory said.

And the last cooky day of each week was for Mrs. Emory's special, own crunchy oatmeal cookies.

On Saturday morning Mrs. Emory went off on a six o'clock bus. Where she went was a mystery. She took a heavy, old suitcase. She came home in the evening on a six o'clock bus. Then the suitcase was heavier.

Charles liked to carry the suitcase to the bus and carry it home again at night. Mrs. Emory always said, "Are you strong enough to carry the suitcase today? It's heavy."

He knew he was strong enough! At the bus he watched Mrs. Emory hop aboard. She was as quick as anything. Her hair was white. Her shoes were old and a little too big. Her coat was long, and so were her skirts. Her hat was green.

Charles handed the heavy suitcase up to her, and she handed him a bag. "Here is your pay, and thank you, Charles Workman. I don't aim to be beholden."

The pay was exactly the same every week—three Monday cookies, two Tuesday cookies, and one each for the other three days.

One Saturday night he waited and waited. "Mom," he called when he came home. "Mrs. Emory is never this late. I wonder where she is."

His mother said, "She's a mystery to me."

Charles shook his head, "I think Mrs. Emory takes those cookies somewhere special."

"Maybe she sells them," suggested his mother. "Are her cookies good enough to sell, Charles?"

"They sure are! I like them a lot and I like Mrs. Emory too. She is one of my best friends. But I do wonder what is making her so late today."

On Sunday morning Charles went over to the kitchen door and peeked in Mrs. Emory's window. The house seemed too still.

"I wonder where she can be?" he asked himself again. "There's no one here."

But behind him, he heard a man say, "Looking for something, boy?" A strange policeman was looking at him.

"I am looking for Mrs. Emory," Charles told him. "She never says where she is going, but she always comes home at night. Her suitcase is very heavy then, and I help her carry it. Last night she never came."

The policeman made some notes in his book. Charles's father came hurrying across the garden. "What is going on here?" Mr. Workman asked.

The policeman answered, "Your son is worried about your neighbor. Quite a detective you have in your family, sir."

"Mrs. Emory? She comes and goes with her old, heavy suitcase. That's all we know about her. She is a neighborhood mystery."

"Oh, Dad," Charles cried. "She's my friend, and I do wonder where she is now!"

The policeman smiled. "She is spending a few days in the City Hospital. She is having a little rest in her other home."

How could a hospital be her home?

The policeman was saying, "Mrs. Emory worked in the hospital kitchen for a long time, making special cookies for children. They liked her cookies best of all."

"So she takes her cookies to children in the hospital. But why is that suitcase so heavy when she comes home?" Charles asked.

"That suitcase is full of special things for making more cookies. The hospital gives them to her," the policeman answered.

"Do they pay her for making the cookies?"

"No, indeed. She likes to do it for the children," the policeman said. "When she needs a rest, she uses a hospital room. She'll be home soon, as lively as ever."

Charles said slowly, "She's going to need me. I'll be waiting for her so I can carry that suitcase. Please tell her I'll be ready."

You Can Depend on Bill

Bill Woodhouse was a good errand boy, so Miss Ada said. Miss Ada had a ladies' dress shop on a busy corner of a city block, and Bill ran errands for her. Bonny Lester and her father lived at the other end of the block, behind their shoe-repair shop.

The busy block was crowded with old buildings and almost too many people. Some of the people didn't know any of the other people who lived on the same block. But Miss Ada and the Lesters and Bill knew each other very well. They depended on each other.

Every school day Bill did a funny kind of errand for Mr. Lester. It was to help Bonny cross the street at Miss Ada's corner, on the way to school.

"Bonny always likes to dilly-dally at that dress-shop window," her father told Bill.

So Bill tried to hurry Bonny. "Don't dilly-dally," he said whenever she stopped at the window. "Those ladies' dresses are too big for you."

"Some day I'll buy one of those dresses with my own money. Wait and see!" she said.

Bill knew about that money. Bonny swept the floor of the shoe-repair shop every day. She kept the pennies and dimes her father gave her in a glass jar. Bill knew that ten jars of pennies and dimes would never buy one of Miss Ada's dresses.

"Ladies' dresses will never fit a little girl," he said.

But Bonny kept on dilly-dallying.

"Why does Bonny spend so much time at my window?" Miss Ada asked Bill.

So he told her. "She's too small for your dresses, Miss Ada. Besides, they cost too much. What can I do about it?"

Miss Ada smiled. "Maybe I can help."

One day she sent Bill on some long errands. When he finished, he was tired. Miss Ada had been making a new dress. Now it was finished. She lifted it up for Bill to see.

"What do you think of this?" she asked.

Bill grinned. "Is it for a little girl?"

Miss Ada nodded. She handed Bill a pair of her pumps. "Run to the shoe shop and tell Mr. Lester I need new heels right away. Bonny can bring the pumps back."

Bill hurried off with the pumps.

It was closing time at the shop. Bonny was sweeping the floor, and Mr. Lester was putting away his tools. "Well," he said. "We can't keep Miss Ada waiting. I'll fix these right now."

"Can Bonny deliver them? I can't wait," said Bill. And he winked at Bonny's father.

To Bonny, Bill said, "Miss Ada is in a hurry for these pumps, so no dilly-dallying at the window."

When the pumps were ready, Bonny ran to the dress shop and rang the bell. Miss Ada and Bill were waiting for her.

Bonny looked around at the beautiful dresses. They were all too big, all but one. That one dress was exactly her size. It was a white dress with pink roses.

Miss Ada held the dress in front of Bonny. "Do you like this dress, Bonny?"

"Oh," Bonny cried. "I want to buy it. I have lots of pennies and dimes in a jar—"

Bill interrupted her, "I'll run and get it."

In no time he came back. Miss Ada counted all the dimes and pennies. "There's enough money in this jar to buy the dress if you want it."

"I want it very much. How did you know I wanted one of your dresses?"

Bonny looked at Bill and guessed the answer. "Bill told you," she said. "My Daddy says you can depend on Bill."

"I depended on Miss Ada," Bill answered.
Miss Ada smiled. "And I depended on Mr.
Lester. We all depend on each other. Isn't
that how it is nowadays?"

Rudolph Is Tired of the City

These buildings are too close to me.
I'd like to PUSH away.
I'd like to live in the country,
And spread my arms all day.

I'd like to spread my breath out, too—
As farmers' sons and daughters do.

I'd tend the cows and chickens.
I'd do the other chores.
Then, all the hours left I'd go
A-SPREADING out-of-doors.

Gwendolyn Brooks

94

Take the Right Road

Help the roadrunner find the rattlesnake. Follow
only the road that has on it words with the same vowel
sounds as the vowel sounds in <u>bite</u> and <u>boat</u>.
Watch the forks in the road. If you take a wrong turn,
go back and try another road.

Animals and People Solve Problems

There are many animal stories in this book. In some stories the animals talk and behave as people do. Sometimes their actions help us understand how people feel about each other.

Other stories are about people like those you know. These stories help us learn more about people. They help us understand the problems people have and how the problems are worked out.

Look at the titles of the stories in Unit 1 and Unit 2. Choose one story in which an animal character finds an answer to his problem. Choose one story in which a boy or girl decides what to do about a problem.

How were the problems in the stories alike?

How were they different?

If you have ever had a problem like the ones in the stories, how did you solve it?

If you have not had a problem like the ones in the stories, tell about one you have had.

Talking without Words

Pretend that, like Ana Rosa, you have just come to the United States and you speak no English. The boys and girls at school do not speak Spanish. You want to tell each other something. How will you do it?

Choose one of the following ideas to tell about. Remember, you cannot understand each other's language.

You will need to act out what you want to tell. Do not say a word. Let the others guess.

1. You have a new bicycle.

2. You dropped a glass and broke it.

3. You smell smoke coming from an upstairs room.

4. You have just seen a ghost.

5. You lost your way coming to school and had to ask for directions.

6. You have peanut butter stuck in the roof of your mouth.

7. Your best friend's dog had puppies, and he gave you one.

Brad's Job

Brad Sanders liked to read signs. They told him what he wanted to know. Brad and his little sister, Pam, were on their way to a new home in Wisconsin. Brad had been reading signs all along the way.

When the family had boarded the big jet plane, Brad's father had said, "Look after your little sister on this trip and keep track of her, Brad. That's your job. We're depending on you."

Now the big jet was coming down through the clouds, and Brad was helping Pam to fasten her seat belt.

The sign had just appeared at the front end of the airplane, and Brad read it aloud to Pam. "Fasten Seat Belts," he read as he fastened hers.

Pam did not help him. She was looking at snowflakes outside the windowpanes of the jet. She had never seen snow before. "Is that snow?" she asked her brother.

"Sure it's snow," Brad said. "We change planes here for Wisconsin. Take my hand, Pam, and don't get lost when we change."

"Don't forget your zipper bag under the seat," his little sister said.

101

What a joke, Brad thought. Of course he wouldn't forget it. That zipper bag was filled with his favorite things. It held his school papers, some baseball playing cards, and his new baseball. He picked up the bag.

"Put on your mittens," he said, "and keep hold of my free hand." Sometimes he did wish Pam could look after herself.

Slowly, the Sanders family moved off the jet and into the airport through a jetway. It was like a hallway without windows. Pam did not like it. She pulled away from Brad.

"Where are we going ?" she cried.

"We are changing planes," he said. "We have to stay with Dad and Mom." With his free hand, Brad clutched his zipper bag.

103

KEY

A. The Sanders family move off the jet and into the airport through a jetway.

B. Mr. Sanders stops at a counter. He looks at a TV screen.

C. The corridor curves to the right. Pam sees a toy shop.

D. Brad finds that he has lost something.

E. Mr. and Mrs. Sanders are waiting at Gate 33.

A.

B.

C.

The big airport was filled with hurrying people and bright lights and wide corridors.

Mr. Sanders pointed to a small TV screen. As new words appeared, Brad read, "Gate 33. Flight 277."

"That's our plane," his father called. "Keep right behind us and hurry."

The corridor curved to the right. Along the way was a toy shop. Behind its windows were lots of dolls.

"Look at the dolls," cried Pam. "I see one of my favorites."

Brad wouldn't let her stop to look.

Pam tugged hard. "Let go!" she cried.

Brad dropped his zipper bag to keep hold of her. But suddenly Pam was gone and so were his father and mother.

There were no signs to show Brad the way.
All around him people rushed by.

Nowhere among them was there a little girl with bright hair.

"I've got to find her," Brad muttered. "Dad told me to keep track of her. That's my special job."

He did not see her in the long corridor, so he dashed into the toy shop for a quick look.

Pam was at a counter, standing on tiptoe and looking at a doll. She saw Brad. "I've found my favorite," Pam said.

Brad grabbed her hand and pulled her back to the corridor. "We've got to find Dad and Mom," he shouted. "Hurry!"

Pam tried to pull away. "Wait, Brad, wait!" she begged. "Where is your zipper bag?"

His bag? His bag with his favorite things!

Brad stared at his empty hand. His voice sounded shaky. "It's gone," he gulped.

Pam did not move. Then her eyes danced.

"Look behind you!" she cried.

Brad whirled around. His zipper bag was just where he had dropped it when Pam pulled away from him. No one had picked it up or taken it away.

Brad reached for it. It was not empty. His favorite things were there. "Thanks, Pam," he said. "You sure have helped me."

Mr. and Mrs. Sanders were already waiting for them at Gate 33. "You're right on time," Mr. Sanders told the children. "Now let's board the plane for Wisconsin."

Christopher the CONTRARY CHAMELEON

Young Christopher Chameleon
   was very, very small;
A scant three inches, nose to tail,
   and less than one inch tall.
Now all chameleon children
   who do as they are told,
Must learn to match their background,
   and are never, never bold.
But Christopher Chameleon
   in a most contrary way,
Refused to change his color
   and just stayed pink all day.

"It makes me tired," said Christopher,
   "to change and change and change.
My head starts getting dizzy,
   and my stomach feels quite strange."
His parents scowled and scolded.
   They said, "This will not do.
You've got to match your background,
   no matter what the hue."
But Christopher Chameleon
   just yawned and said, "I think
I'll take a nap on this green leaf,"
   and stayed the same bright pink.

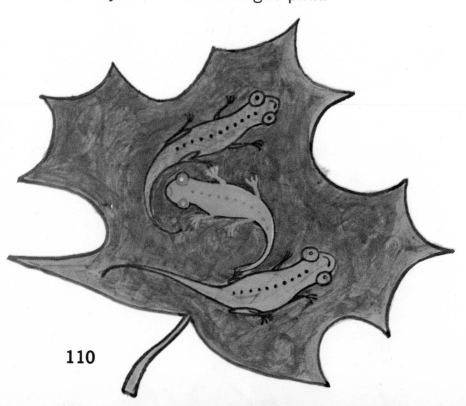

The rest of the chameleons
  matched places where they lay.
But drowsing little Christopher
  stood out as plain as day.
And so, a big crow sitting
  on a nearby maple tree
Saw something bright upon a leaf
  and swooped down close to see.
Christopher felt a shadow
  blocking out the sun
And opened one bright eye and knew
  the time had come to run!
Beneath the leaf he darted,
  as fast as he could go,
And then he clung there hoping
  that he had lost the crow.

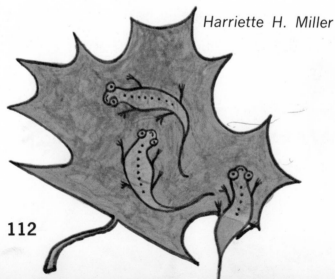

"I'm sure I spotted something,"
  croaked the crow from quite nearby.
"It looked like a pink lizard
  from up there in the sky."
"That crow saw me," thought Christopher,
  "from way up in the air.
He did not see the others,
  but he knew that I was there."
The crow flapped off, and Christopher
  peeked out, and when he'd seen
That it was safe, climbed on his leaf
  and quickly turned quite green.

Harriette H. Miller

Mr. Blynn's Crazy Kite

Andy and his friends were playing ball on the Campbells' farm. It was almost too windy to play ball. The sun was already setting. It was bright, bright red.

Andy was catching a ball. Up it sailed high into the air, and down it came into his mitt.

"Wow!" Andy Campbell and Ed Miller shouted.

Mrs. Campbell was watching from the back porch of the house. "You have far-seeing eyes, Andy," she said.

It was true. Andy's far-seeing eyes could find beetles touring around a meadow. He could see small birds hiding in the leaves of a tree. And when Mr. Blynn's kites sailed high in the air, Andy could track them touring across the sky.

Mr. Blynn was a farmer. When he finished his farm work, he made kites in a small workshop in an open meadow.

Some of the kites were five feet long. They had strange shapes. One was a big flat owl. One was curved at both ends.

Andy's favorite kite looked like a huge arrowhead. One end was pointed. The other end looked like a pair of wings.

It was fun watching Mr. Blynn fly his kites. Sometimes they dipped and crashed. Sometimes they flew out of sight. A few of them broke loose. Andy's far-seeing eyes helped Mr. Blynn track them across the sky.

Those far-seeing eyes helped Andy to catch balls pretty well too.

Mrs. Campbell called, "Do your best now, Andy. Time for one more throw. It's already suppertime." Then she went into the house.

"Throw the ball as high as you can," Bobby Brown yelled. "We'll try to catch it."

The ball soared into the air. Andy watched it go. Suddenly a strange object appeared in the sky. It glowed with reddish light.

What a queer thing it was! It looked like a saucer with a cup upside down on it.

Andy forgot about catching the ball. He stared and stared at the strange object. The other boys were staring at it too.

Bobby said, "Say, is that thing a flying saucer?" He ran across fields trying to keep up with the strange moving object.

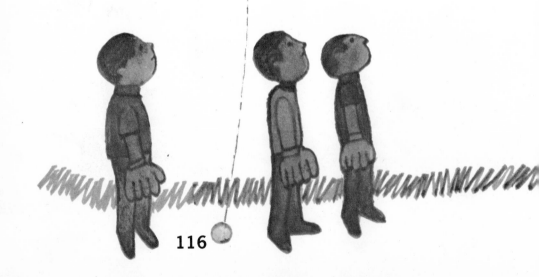

Mrs. Campbell called, "What's going on?"

Ed Miller jumped up and down. He pointed at the object. "Call the police, Mrs. Campbell. There's a flying saucer!"

Andy's far-seeing eyes were already tracking the reddish glow. "Mr. Blynn will want to see this," he decided.

So Andy hopped on his bike and headed for Mr. Blynn's meadow.

Mr. Blynn was standing in the meadow and staring up at the strange object. In one hand he held some loose twine, and he was laughing to himself.

"Well, boy," Mr. Blynn said to Andy, "what do you think that is up there?"

"Is it a flying saucer?" Andy wondered. "With a cabin on top? It looks like one, all reddish and moving so fast."

"Wind's moving fast too," Mr. Blynn answered. "Did you notice that?"

"I forgot about the wind," Andy said.

"There's enough wind to give a kite a good lift of air," Mr. Blynn said. "A good lift of air is what makes it fun to fly a kite. I like to see what happens then."

Andy said slowly, "But that thing doesn't look like a kite, does it? What's that reddish light in the top part of it?"

The strange object was moving farther and farther away from them.

"Take one last look," Mr. Blynn suggested.

Andy squinted. "Maybe that is your kite, sir. I can see the pointed end and the wings. But what about that thing on top?"

Mr. Blynn smiled. "Maybe my kite and a weather balloon got mixed up with each other. Maybe they tangled. I guess a small instrument on the balloon tangled with my kite string and the kite broke loose."

Mr. Blynn let the loose string hang from his hand. He said, "Yes, sir, the kite broke loose, and the wind is carrying those two along together. That's my guess."

Andy had another question. "But how about that reddish light?"

Mr. Blynn winked. "Did you notice how red the sun was when it was setting?"

"Yes, sir. I noticed it when I was catching a ball over at the farm."

"Well," Mr. Blynn said, "I guess the balloon-kite was up high too. High enough to catch some of the sun's reddish light."

Mr. Blynn looked at Andy and winked again. "That's your flying saucer, boy."

They both laughed.

"Yes, sir, Mr. Blynn, I guess it is. I'll go and tell the boys." And off went Andy to tell the news.

VALENTINE
FOR EARTH

Oh, it will be fine
To rocket through space
And see the reverse
Of the moon's dark face.

To travel to Saturn
Or Venus or Mars,
Or maybe discover
Some uncharted stars.

But do they have anything
Better than we ?
Do you think, for instance,
They have a blue sea

For sailing and swimming ?
Do the planets have hills
With raspberry thickets
Where a song sparrow fills

The summer with music ?
And do they have snow
To silver the roads
Where the school buses go ?

Oh, I'm all for rockets
And worlds cold or hot
But I'm wild in love
With the planet we've got !

Frances Frost

122

THE NEIGHBORHOOD NEWS

Have You Seen Tim's Surprise?

The Neighborhood News thanks the boys and girls of Spring Street School for their letters about the surprise that Tim Walker left for the neighborhood.

Spring Street School is a block from where the new freeway is to go. Many houses near the school have been torn down to make room for it.

Tim Walker's house was torn down, and his family moved away. So Tim left a surprise gift for his school friends.

The Neighborhood News is happy to print these letters and pictures.

Mark Topping
EDITOR

Dear Mr. Topping,

Do you know about Baker Street ?

Machines came and plowed into all the houses. The machines tore up sidewalks and grass and trees.

They carted everything away, but they did leave a pile of old pipes.

The pipes were bent and crooked. They were part of old sprinklers. They gave me an idea. It's fun to make new things out of old junk, so I used them to make a surprise for my friends.

Yours truly,

Tim Walker

P.S. Of course, Dan and Sam and Linda helped me.

Dear Mr. Topping,

We call our new play place Triangle Park. It has three corners, and it looks like a triangle. It's a pretty small place but it's just right for Tim's surprise.

Tim had the idea. We helped him stick the pipes into the ground. We made the pipes look like a forest. They were like trees—crooked and straight and tall and short.

"A pipe forest," Sam shouted.

He'll write about that.

Yours for the pipe forest,

Dan Tyler

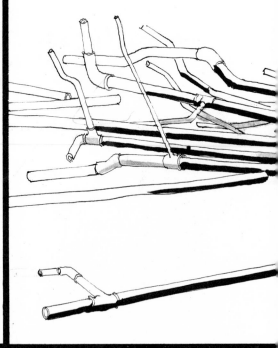

127

Dear Mr. Topping,

It's fun to crawl around a pipe forest. We crawled in ours with our eyes closed. Once we bumped into a big pipe. It hit three more, and the whole forest toppled over.

Tim just stuck the pipes into the ground again. This time we crawled with our eyes open and ran races.

After that we were clowns in a circus. We were pretty silly.

Linda had a new idea. She will tell about that.

Yours,
Sam Pond

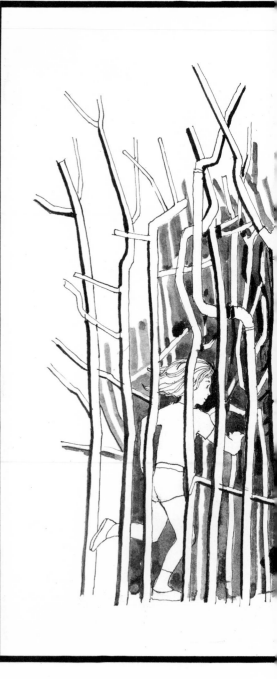

128

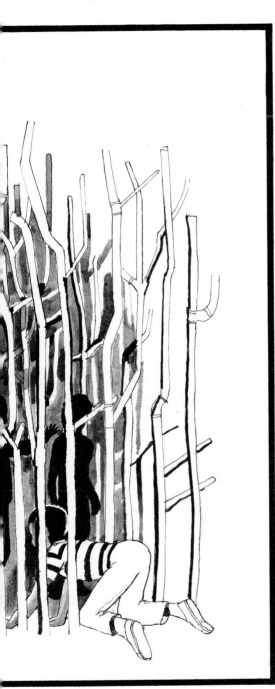

Dear Mr. Topping,

I like horses, so I thought Tim's surprise could be a circus ring for horses.

Horses prance and play tricks in a circus ring. They stand on their hind feet and dance. I was a horse first, doing tricks. Then Dan and Sam decided to be horses too, dancing and prancing.

Please come and see Tim's surprise. Everyone is welcome. The pipes may topple over. If they do, we will set them up again in a new way.

Tell people that Tim's surprise is for everyone.

Yours for fun,
Linda Lamb

THE NEIGHBORHOOD NEWS

**Dear Linda and Sam and
Dan and Tim,**

Congratulations !

I have just seen Tim's
surprise.

It is not old piping now.

It is a forest and a
circus ring and a thing
of beauty for Springdale.

Yours for Triangle Park,

Mark Topping
EDITOR, NEIGHBORHOOD NEWS

130

SPECIAL VISITORS

One summer Jeff and his family went to Colorado. Their cabin was high in the Rocky Mountains. It was near big woods, where hummingbirds live in the trees.

"They are so tiny and they fly so fast," Jeff said to his father. "How can I ever see what they look like?"

"We can set up a feeder for the hummingbirds," his father said. "We will set it up here at the cabin. Then some tiny hummers will surely come."

131

That summer Jeff often watched the hummingbirds. Day after day they came to sip the sweet red liquid in the feeder.

One day a beautiful male broad-tail came to the feeder. It sipped the sweet red liquid and was gone with a flash of its whirring wings. Then something like a tiny green helicopter moved through the air. A plain buffy-breasted hummer was coming to taste the red food. The flashy male whirred down and chased the buffy-breasted hummer into the woods. Back he came with a noisy whirr and perched on a limb of the tree.

Over and over that bossy male broad-tail chased away the other birds. Finally one hummingbird led the male far away through the trees. Other hummingbirds came and fed, until the bossy male chased them off.

"Where do they go in the woods?" Jeff wondered. "I wish I could find their nests."

Jeff had seen pictures of hummingbirds' nests in books. But he did want to see a real nest. He knew they were very small. He knew they were hard to find in the woods.

Day after day Jeff tracked a special path through the woods. He followed the birds when they left the feeder. He followed their flashing colors among the trees. He listened for their whirring wings. But summer was going fast, and he was still looking for a hummingbird's nest.

One chilly morning Jeff left the cabin after breakfast. He had on his red shirt. Hummingbirds like the color red. They often come near it, as they did to the feeder.

Jeff walked along his special path. He heard the hummers. Whirring wings came near. A tiny hummingbird was coming toward Jeff's red shirt. The bird dipped once. The whirring sound stopped. Jeff felt a fairy-like touch on his arm.

Then the buffy-breasted green hummer flew off to feed on some red flowers.

Jeff waited. When the tiny bird flew off into the woods, he tried to follow. He pushed through low branches of the trees. The nest must be near! But he could not find it.

He turned to leave the woods, and there was the nest close enough to touch. It was only as big as a nutshell. It looked like the other knots on the tree branch. But this knot was a nest. A hummingbird was in it.

Jeff walked around the nest. The small buffy-breasted mother's eyes followed him. She made little frightened fluttery sounds. Jeff stepped still closer. Away she flew. He tiptoed up and peeked down into the nest. He saw two very tiny eggs. They looked like small white beans.

Jeff reached out to touch them. He stopped, jamming his hands into his pockets. "No!" he said to himself, "I won't touch them."

He turned away from the nest. Very, very slowly, Jeff walked home.

He was late for lunch. His mother asked, "Where have you been all morning, Jeff?"

"Oh, in the woods. Dad, how long does it take for a baby hummingbird to fly?"

"Quite a while, Jeff."

"Can babies eat out of our feeder?"

"Yes, if they have a wire to perch on."

"Dad, will you help me put a wire perch on our feeder?"

"Sure, Jeff." With a smile his father asked, "Are you waiting for special visitors?"

"I just want to be ready," Jeff answered.

He helped his father bend a wire around the feeding tube. He kept the feeder filled. Hummingbirds came and went from the feeder. For quite a while every day, Jeff watched them sip the sweet colored liquid.

"How about those special visitors?" his Dad asked. "It's about time for them to come, isn't it?"

"Maybe," Jeff said. It was hard to wait and to keep on watching. But he did do it.

One morning a mother hummer and two baby hummers did come to the feeder. Jeff watched the babies with their short bills. One at a time the tiny hummers perched on the wire. They sipped the sweet red liquid.

Then they followed the mother bird into the woods. Jeff watched them go.

"Gee, I'm glad you hatched!" he called.

Like a Bug

Do you ever wonder
what it's like to be a bug,

Fitted in a jacket
that is stiff and rather snug,

Sleeping in a thistle
or beneath a leafy rug,

Never having gingersnaps
or cocoa in a mug,

Or a father you can talk to,
or a puppy you can hug?

Aileen Fisher

130

Breaking a Code

The boys in the clubhouse weren't happy. They had been robbed! All their candy and other food was gone.

"How could anyone know where I hid the stuff?" asked David. "I wanted you to find it, but no one else. So, just like always, I wrote a note in our code. It told you where I hid it. See, here is the note."

3c3a   4c5d   7b2d   8c1c3a

Paul shook his head. "I can't see how they knew. I can't read this without our code sheet." He walked to the apple box that the boys used for a desk. "Hey, fellows," he called. "Our code sheet is missing!"

"Somebody found it and figured out where David hid the stuff," said Jim.

"And now they have our code sheet," added Paul. "We'll just have to think of a new club code."

David said, "It should be one we can keep in our heads. Then we won't have to worry about other kids finding it."

Jim came up with an idea. On a piece of paper he printed this:

Uif   dboez   jt   jo   uif   bqqmf   cpy.

The boys looked at each other. No one could read the sentence. Jim said, "If you know the alphabet you can do it."

The boys tried to read the sentence again. They wondered what the alphabet had to do with it.

Suddenly Paul cried, "I've got it. *Uif* says *The.*"

Jim said, "You're right! Now we don't have to write out a code that other kids can find."

Can you read what Jim printed?

Can you print a message in this code?

Can you make up a code?

The Old Code

The boys were going to the playground. Bob picked up a rumpled piece of paper. "Hey," he called. "I found our old code."

"It's no good now," Jim said. "The other club knows about it."

"But I still have your message," Dave said. "Let me see if I can decode it."

Dave decoded the note: 3c3a 4c5d 7b2d 8c1c3a. "Now I know where those boys found the candy," he said.

	a	b	c	d
1	g	sn	a	tch
2	r	sn	e	ead
3	n	spr	i	igh
4	s	st	o	er
5	m	tr	u	ld
6	f	str	oa	y
7	t	br	ea	nd
8	j	scr	c	th

This is the code David used.
Can you decode the note?
Maybe this will help.

1a5c5a is **gum**
6a5c3a is **fun**
7a4c5d is **told**

Now read these sentences.

1a2c7a 7b2d 1c7d 8a1c5a.
3b2d 8a1c5a 4c3a 7b2d.
2a2d6d 1c7a 7a2c3a.
6a2c1d 5a4c5a.

A Crazy Flight

The world is lazy turning
When you wait.
The sun, a silly tortoise, crawls across today.
The moon stares down more than three hundred nights:
But then, for one quick happy day
A birthday day—they spin and fly.
It's hard to wait.

All earth things change.
Brown trees turn green.
And somewhere I have seen
A rocket out of range;

Your rocket, flying past the moon
and into sun. And with a satellite
And you—in space;
I wish you, child, a crazy flight.

Myra Cohn Livingston

THE SCOOTER

When Bert was almost seven years old, he wanted a bicycle more than anything else in the whole world. The trouble was, he knew he would have to give up his faithful old scooter if ever his wish for a bike did come true. Bert hated to say good-by to things he liked.

One Saturday morning Bert was helping his mother clean out the garage. "We need more room in here, Bert," his mother said. "Let's move this big old cardboard carton."

The old carton was heavy, but with Bert's help they finally pushed it to the back wall of the garage.

"Thank you," Mother said. "You are getting bigger and stronger every day."

Bert nodded. He was big enough right now to have a bicycle, and in a few days he was going to be a whole year older. He knew what he wanted more than anything else for his birthday. And that great day was coming soon.

Bert's old playthings were piled up along one side of the garage wall. His mother was looking at them.

"Isn't it about time to throw away these old things?" she asked.

Bert looked at the balls piled in a big basket. There were at least ten of them. He looked at a box filled with trucks and cars and trains, and he sighed. They were pretty old, but he still liked them.

Then he looked at his scooter. It was all by itself and leaning against a wall. Bert went over and patted his faithful old scooter. He hated to say good-by to things that he liked, especially his scooter. So he didn't answer his mother's question.

"I guess I'll go for a ride," he said. Bert hopped on the scooter and zoomed along the walk by Mike Jones's house on the corner.

"Hi!" Bert shouted to Mike as he zoomed by him.

Mike was always waiting on the walk, but he never answered. Every time Bert raced by on the scooter, Mike just looked at the scooter. He never spoke a word to Bert.

Bert cut a fancy circle around Mike's driveway and zoomed back to the garage.

"I never want to say good-by to you," he told his faithful old friend, as he cut another fancy circle and jumped off the scooter.

But he did hope his mom and dad would know that he was old enough for a birthday bicycle now.

Finally the great day came. It was Saturday, and when Bert sat down at the breakfast table, he found a big birthday card. It was propped up against his box of corn flakes. Bert's father was a cartoonist. He had drawn a funny picture of a cat and the cat was saying, "HAPPY *BERT*DAY! NOW FOLLOW MEEOW!" Fastened to one of the cat's paws was an especially long string of red yarn.

Bert did not stop to eat his corn flakes. He jumped up from the table. He started to follow the string to find his *BERT*day gift, without saying a word. He began to track the yarn.

He tracked the red yarn under tables, behind three chairs, into one room, and out of another. The yarn took Bert through the kitchen door and down the back steps of the house.

At last the string of red yarn led Bert into the open garage. It led him over to the back wall. It stopped behind the big old cardboard carton.

And there behind the carton, bright and shining and beautiful, was a "new" secondhand bike. Leaning against the wall beside the bike was Bert's faithful old scooter.

Bert untied the string from the bike and stood there. He looked at its shiny red frame, but he put his hands on the steering board of the scooter and jumped aboard.

Out of the garage Bert zoomed on the scooter, like a jet stream. Mike Jones was waiting, as usual, to watch Bert zoom by and cut a fancy circle in the driveway.

This time Bert surprised him. Bert cut an especially fancy circle around Mike and made the scooter stop.

Off hopped Bert. He handed the scooter over to Mike Jones. "It's yours now, for keeps," Bert told him.

Then, running as fast as he could run, Bert headed for the garage. He saw his mom and dad watching him as he raced by the house.

But he didn't stop running toward the garage. Over his shoulder he called to them, "First I had to take my little old scooter for a good-by ride. What a nifty bike! Thanks. It's just what I wanted for my BERTday."

Bears Aren't Everywhere [1]

One night Danny's mother read him a book about bears. The book was about brown bears and black bears, cinnamon bears and a polar bear.

Then Danny's mother put out the light and said, "Good night, sleep tight, Danny."

But Danny did not sleep tight.

Danny lay in bed and thought about bears.

153

All of a sudden bears were everywhere—brown bears, black bears, cinnamon bears. And a polar bear was at the window.

Danny put his head under the covers, and the bears went away.

The next morning Danny forgot all about the bears. He helped his father feed the chickens and bring in the eggs from the nests. Then Danny went exploring.

He climbed the hill behind the farmhouse. He stood high on the hill and looked down on the farm below. The cold wind blew in his face.

Danny saw that everything was changing. The goldenrod had changed from gold to golden brown. The leaves on some of the trees were changing from green to orange, red, and yellow.

Then Danny ran down the hill to the orchard. He saw that the apples were changing too. They were turning from sour green to red and yellow.

Danny did some exploring. He looked into the hole where a woodchuck lived. But the woodchuck wasn't at home.

"I think the woodchuck must be out eating someplace," said Danny to himself. "He wants to get as fat as he can, so that he can have a good sleep in the winter."

Danny climbed over the old stone wall, but just as he got to the edge of the woods, he heard a noise.

What kind of a noise was that—or was it a noise at all?

It wasn't a bong or a bang.

It was more of a crackle or crunch.

Danny thought about bears—brown bears, black bears, cinnamon bears, and the polar bear he had seen at his window.

Danny turned around.

He walked like an Indian, as quietly as he could walk, over the old stone wall, through the orchard.

Then he ran. Danny ran as fast as he could run.

"There's a bear down there," yelled Danny to his mother, as he slammed the kitchen door.

When Danny's father came in from milking the cows that night, Danny said, "There's a bear down there."

"Where, down there?" asked Danny's father.

"Down below the orchard in the woods," Danny answered.

"Then you and I will go down to the woods in the morning and find him," Danny's father said.

But Danny didn't want to go down to the woods with his father. He didn't want to go exploring and find the bear.

When Danny went to bed that night, the bears were everywhere—brown bears, black bears, cinnamon bears, and the polar bear at the window.

"What kind of a bear is waiting in the woods down there?" said Danny to himself.

Then he put his head under the covers, and the bears all went away.

When Danny woke up in the morning, he couldn't see a thing. The fields, the trees, the barn—all the world around his house was covered with a soft white fog.

No wind was blowing. Everything was still.

"Come on, Danny," Danny's father said after breakfast. "We're going down to find the bear."

"Not this morning," Danny said. "I have to feed the chickens and bring in the eggs."

"Oh, no," Danny's father said. "I need you, Danny. I need you to show me where the bear is hiding in the woods."

So Danny had to go with his father to the woods to find the bear.

Danny and his father walked down the hill together. They walked in the still white fog.

"Like ghosts," said Danny.

"No, Indians," his father said. "Put your feet down carefully. Don't make any noise."

When they came to the orchard, Danny and his father stood still and listened.

And sure enough !

Danny heard the noise again.

It wasn't a bong or a bang.

It was more of a crackle and crunch.

"There's the bear," Danny said very softly.

A soft wind blew.

The white fog swirled around.

Danny and his father stood very still and listened.

Danny didn't want to go exploring over the old stone wall and into the woods. Danny just wanted to run home as fast as he could run. He wanted to slam the kitchen door.

But Danny's father took his hand, and they went over the wall and into the woods together.

There was the noise again.

Not a bong or a bang, but a crackle and crunch, in the dry leaves scattered on the ground.

Danny stopped and looked and listened.

Just then a fat gray squirrel ran up the trunk of a great big walnut tree. When the squirrel leaped from branch to branch to branch, he shook walnuts down. They fell with a crunch and crackle into the dry leaves scattered on the ground.

Danny laughed and so did his father.

"Some bear," Danny said.

His father smiled. "I guess bears aren't really everywhere, are they, Danny?"

"I guess not," Danny said.

"And don't you think," said Danny's father, "that it would be better to be SURE it's a bear, before you get so frightened of a bear that's not even there?"

Danny knew that his father was right.

"My bear was just a fat gray squirrel getting ready for winter," Danny said.

"That's a good idea," said his father.

So Danny and his father filled their pockets full of walnuts and took them home to dry.

A long time after that Danny sat beside the fire and cracked his walnuts, while the wind blew against the window and the snow was deep outside.

"I wonder," Danny said, "if underneath the snow someplace, or in some hollow tree—"

"A big brown bear is waiting for you?" Danny's father said.

"No," laughed Danny, "but I wonder if underneath the snow someplace, or in some hollow tree, that fat gray squirrel is eating walnuts just like me?"

A PET NAMED JET

One morning when Judy came to her new school on Pepper Street, the children were chasing a stray cat. It was black and thin, and Judy felt sorry for it. A boy named Ross caught the cat and lifted it by the back of the neck. It hung like dirty worn-out fur.

"It's an old tomcat," Ross said. "Let's wash him off." He started for the drinking fountain.

"Stop it!" Judy cried. She put her lunch down, ran after Ross, and pulled at his arm. The cat jumped free and began to run.

163

Ross was angry. All at once he said, "Black cats are bad luck! Don't let him cross your path!"

The children ran, and Judy was glad when the cat got away.

At lunch time, as Judy started to look for her lunch, she heard some children laughing. Then she saw Ross hiding her sandwich. When she ran at him, he acted afraid.

"Don't cross my path!" he shouted.

The other children ran away when Judy came near, and Judy felt angry. She wanted her sandwich! Just then a teacher came out.

"What's going on?" she asked.

"Nothing, Miss Downs," the children said.

"Nothing, Miss Downs," said Judy, trying not to cry.

Miss Downs looked upset. Judy liked Miss Downs.

But Judy said to herself, "The children at this school don't like me. Miss Downs can't change that!"

164

"Come inside, Judy," Miss Downs said softly.

As they went in, Kim handed Judy a paper bag. "I hope you'll like what's in the bag, Judy," she said, trying to be friendly.

All Judy wanted was to be back at her old school, with her old friends.

After school Judy took a short cut home through an alley. She saw the same cat lying in the dirt. He was thin and scrawny. His eyes were big and gold. Judy tried to pet him, but the big scrawny tomcat stayed out of reach. When she started on, he followed her along the alley.

Judy coaxed him into her house with some scraps of meat. The cat ate them and yowled for more.

"My, my!" said Judy's mother. "That cat hasn't had anything to eat for days!"

Judy gave him a saucer of milk. "May I keep him, Mama?" she asked, pouring more milk into the saucer.

In her mind Judy saw him fat and glossy.

Her father laughed. "You can try," he said. "But that old tomcat may have something to say about anybody keeping him."

Judy bent over and patted the cat. "I'll call him Jet," she said, "like the buttons on Mama's black coat."

After dinner she tried to pet him, but Jet jumped down. The scrawny old tomcat curled up at her feet, tucking his tail under himself. Oh, how Judy wanted Jet to be her pet.

"That is one proud cat," said her father. "You'll never make a lap-cat out of him."

166

Every day after that Jet met Judy in the alley. Every day she fed and brushed him. His coat grew silky. His bones no longer showed. Still he would not lie on her lap.

Judy said to herself, "Jet is my friend just the same."

At school Ross still teased her, and Judy still chased him. Sometimes Ross would hide her lunch, and someone would laugh. That made Judy angry.

One day Judy found Jet sitting on the alley fence. The sun shone on his fur and his eyes were slits of gold. As Judy came up, a man shouted, "Scat, cat!" He threw some water at Jet.

Judy ran to pick him up, but Jet darted away. A man called over the fence, "If that's your cat, keep him out of my yard."

Judy looked up and down the alley for Jet. Then she walked along calling, "Jet! Jet!" The cat was gone. Judy cried as she walked home. Would she ever see Jet again?

167

When she reached home, there lay Jet, stretched out by the kitchen stove, washing himself.

"He's been home quite a while," said her mother. "He was sopping wet."

Judy picked Jet up and hugged him. "Poor Jet!" she said.

She brushed him before dinner. After dinner she brushed him some more. When his fur shone again, she put down the brush.

"Now," she said, "he'll let me pet him."

But the cat jumped down, stretched, then curled up at her feet as he always did. Judy sighed, "Is he really my friend, Papa?"

Her father laughed. "He is your friend. He's just too proud to sit in your lap."

Judy wondered about that word. "What is 'proud'?" she asked.

"'Proud' to that cat," said her father, "means he doesn't care what other people think about him."

Judy's eyes filled. "But I love him," she said.

"And he loves you. But if you didn't love him," said her father, "that old cat wouldn't cry about it. Because he likes himself just the way he is. He says, 'I'm Jet. You can take me or leave me.'"

Judy thought about being proud. She wished she could be like Jet. She would say, "Take me or leave me. I'm Judy."

Then she thought, "I am Judy! I will be proud, like Jet."

The next morning she made two lunches. At school she left one on a bench and hid the other in her coat. Kim and another girl were playing hop-scotch near the bench.

"May I play too?" Judy asked.

Kim said, "All right." The other girl walked off. Judy was hurt, but this time she did not cry or get angry.

"I'm Judy," she thought. "You can take me or leave me."

170

Kim smiled and said, "You can be first."

As they played, there was an angry shout, and then they heard boys laughing. Judy looked. Ross had her lunch again. This time he bit into the sandwich, made a face, and spit out the food.

"What's wrong with Ross?" Kim asked.

Judy laughed. "Maybe he doesn't like the soap flakes I put in my sandwich today."

Miss Downs came out. "What's going on?" she called.

"Nothing," Ross sputtered. He didn't look at Judy.

"Nothing, Miss Downs," said the other children, laughing.

"Well, come inside," Miss Downs said. "Judy, I'm glad to see you have a lunch today."

Miss Downs was smiling at Judy, as if she were thinking, "You're Judy—and I'll take you."

172

JUST FOR YOU

It was another summer day.
It began with a picnic
In the woods.

After I ate my jelly sandwich,
I drank two cups of very sweet lemonade.

The other people were taking naps
So I walked away.

173

I walked and walked.

I picked a few blue flowers.

They looked like stars.

I tasted a few pine needles.

I laughed and laughed with a squirrel

who was dancing around and around

an oak tree.

Then I turned backward and did not know

where to go.

I was alone.

174

I ran through the woods.

And there I was in the middle of a circle of tall trees and tiny daisies.

I lay down on the warm earth.

Very soon, bees hummed overhead.

A beetle toured my right toe.

A round, brown bird hopped across my stomach.

And I was my self in a world of grass.

I was so happy I fell asleep.

Sometime later, someone called my name.

So I got up and ran to the voice. It was time to go home.

Now when the days are all gray, and the trees have no leaves, and the grass is brown with winter,

I remember my meadow.

I see what the colors were, and how the smells smelled.

Any time, anywhere, I can shut my eyes and go there and be happy.

I give you my meadow.

Julia W. Cunningham

THE INVITATION

Nancy Ann walked down the country road. She was on her way home from school. In her hand was a picture of the schoolhouse, cut out of red paper. On it was written: "Come to the fair! At Lone Oak School, Saturday at 2 o'clock."

Michael caught up with her. He and Nancy Ann were both in the second grade. They lived near each other, and they often walked home together.

177

He saw what was in her hand. "Is that an invitation to our fair?" he asked.

"Yes," she said.

"What are you going to do with it?" he asked.

"I know what I'd *like* to do with it," she said. "I'd like to throw it away."

He looked surprised. "Why?" he asked.

"Because it's for Mrs. Peacham, that's why," said Nancy Ann. "The teacher says we should invite her because she's new here. I go past her house on the way home, so I have to give her this invitation and tell her about the fair!" Nancy Ann made a face.

"Don't you like her?" asked Michael.

"No, I don't," said Nancy Ann.

"But you don't even know her, do you?" asked Michael.

"I know her well enough," said Nancy Ann. "I went past her farm last month, and I thought I saw a pony. I went closer, and it *was* a pony, tied under an apple tree. I was going to pet him, and just then old Mrs. Peacham came running out of the house. She waved her arms and said, 'Stop. Don't take any of those apples!'"

"You weren't going to, were you?" asked Michael.

"Of course I wasn't," said Nancy Ann. "I told her I wasn't, and then I ran home."

"And now you have to go back," said
Michael.

"Yes," said Nancy Ann. "I don't see why
the teacher couldn't have asked someone
else."

They came to Mrs. Peacham's farm. It was
a small farm, with a house almost hidden by
trees. A lane led to the house.

Michael waited while Nancy Ann went
down the lane. The house was quiet. She
stood on the porch for a little while, but she
did not knock. She put the invitation
down in front of the door. Then she
tiptoed away.

She went back to the road. "There!"
she said. "I left the invitation."

"Wasn't she at home?" asked Michael.

"I don't know," said Nancy Ann.

180

Come to the
fair!

Hans Zander

"I thought you were supposed to *give* her the invitation," said Michael. "I thought you were supposed to tell her about the fair."

"I was," said Nancy Ann, "but I didn't want her to come out and shout at me."

They walked down the road. Michael asked, "Did you promise the teacher to stop and tell Mrs. Peacham about the fair?"

Nancy Ann began to walk more slowly. "I did promise," she said. "I'd better go back."

"I'll go back with you," said Michael.

They went back to Mrs. Peacham's. They walked down the lane. The invitation was where Nancy Ann had left it. She picked it up and knocked at the door. Michael stood beside her.

A little old woman opened the door. She put her head on one side like a bird, and looked at them.

"I brought you this, Mrs. Peacham," said Nancy Ann. She held out the invitation.

Mrs. Peacham took it. "I can't read it without my glasses," she said.

"It's an invitation—to our fair at school," said Nancy Ann. "We're going to have an art show—and songs—and games."

"Didn't you come to see me one day?" asked Mrs. Peacham. "Didn't you run away before I could talk to you?"

"I—I didn't think you wanted me here," said Nancy Ann. "You thought I was taking your apples—and I wasn't. All I wanted was to see the pony."

"You didn't take any apples?" said Mrs. Peacham. "That's good, because they were green. I was afraid you might take a bite of a green apple and have a stomachache. There's nothing worse than a green-apple stomachache. But the apples are ripe now. Why don't you two go and pick some?"

"Thank you, we will," said Michael.

They went around the house to the apple tree. The branches were hanging down with big red apples. And under the tree was the pony. His sides were fat. His brown coat shone in the sunlight.

"Oh, he's beautiful!" said Nancy Ann.

"His name is Sam," said Mrs. Peacham. "Would you like to ride him?"

"Could we?" asked Nancy Ann.

"Yes," said Mrs. Peacham. "Just climb on. Sam will know what to do."

Michael helped Nancy Ann up on the pony's back. The pony trotted around the apple tree. He ran in two neat circles before he stopped.

Then Michael took his turn.

184

"I used to keep ponies in the city," said Mrs. Peacham. "I used to run a pony ride in the park for boys and girls. But my rheumatism got worse. I couldn't help the boys and girls off and on any more, so I sold my ponies, all but Sam. He was my favorite. When I came to the country to live, I just had to bring him with me."

"I'm sorry about your rheumatism," said Nancy Ann. "Will you be well enough to come to the fair?"

"I'm much better in the country," said Mrs. Peacham. "If I do come to the fair, could Sam come? I think he misses the boys and girls. Besides, he needs exercise. You and your friends could have free rides."

"That would really be wonderful!" said Nancy Ann.

"Ask your teacher how she likes the idea," said Mrs. Peacham, "and let me know what she says."

"Our teacher will like it," said Michael. "She couldn't help liking it."

"Now," said Mrs. Peacham, "why don't we pick some apples?"

So they picked apples and sat under the tree to eat them.

"It's like a picnic," said Nancy Ann. "Here, Sam, come to the picnic."

And the pony came straight to where they were sitting and joined the picnic, and ate an apple too.

LET'S
MAKE UP A STORY

It's fun to make up stories. It's more fun to make up funny stories. I wish we could make up a funny story together. Will you help me? And will you think up a name for our story?

How shall we begin? Once upon a time?

We'll need a main character. You can think up a funny name for her, can't you?

Are you ready now? Then let's begin.

Once upon a time there was a cow named _____. She didn't live on a farm. She lived in the city. She lived in the backyard of a house where a boy and a girl lived. Their names were _____ and _____.

Every story should have a problem to be worked out. What will our problem be?

Let's say that the boy and girl don't like to drink milk. That's not funny at all. But it is a problem for the cow, because if young _____ and _____ won't drink the milk, the family will sell _____. She wants to go on living in the backyard. She likes the boy and girl. If only she can get _____ and _____ to like milk, all will be well.

So one day the cow strayed into the backyard strawberry patch and ate up all the strawberries.

That's not funny one bit. But wait. What do you suppose happened the next morning when the little girl was told to milk the cow?

Why _____, the cow, gave strawberry milk shakes ! The children liked strawberry milk shakes. They liked the cow too—especially when they fed her a chocolate bar. I'm sure you can guess what happened. That's right. _____ gave chocolate milk shakes. But the best was yet to come. On _____'s birthday, the cow ate ice cubes—and gave ice cream !

By this time the family no longer talked of selling their backyard cow. The children were drinking so much milk their cheeks grew rosy. And the cow grew famous.

People came from miles around to gaze at our main character, _____, the cow. By that time the two children had made up all kinds of secret flavors. Can you think of some flavors you would especially like ?

COUNTRY FAIR
JULY 20-23

One of the drinks people liked best was cherry milk shakes. Another was sweet-pickle ice cream with strawberries.

When the family decided to enter _____ in the country fair, they fed her _____ and ice cubes. Then they loaded her in a truck and drove over bumpy roads to the fair. It was a hot day and everything went wrong. Our two characters, _____ and _____, told the crowd that their wonderful cow would give _____ ice cream. But the heat had melted the ice cubes and the bumpy road had churned _____'s milk. The best the cow could give was two pounds of _____ butter. It tasted terrible.

The poor cow was so upset she broke loose. She knocked over the hot-dog booth and ate up all the buns. To coax her back to her stall, _____ fed her peanuts. The cow had never tasted peanuts before, but she took a liking to them. In no time at all she was giving peanut-butter sandwiches.

She won a first prize for her peanut-butter sandwiches. The family drove home and lived happily ever after.

So the characters in this story did work out their problem, didn't they? As for _____, the cow, perhaps she is munching popcorn. I wonder what she will make with that.

191

Reading a Picture Story

A rebus story uses pictures instead of words. In the story below you will need to use each pair of pictures to make one word. See if you can read this funny story.

A ⁓⁓⁓ + 👤 was swimming by a

🔺 + 🚢 . Through the window

he saw a 🐉 + 🪰 push over a

lighted 🕯️ + 🌿 on the

🪑 + 🌰 . The 🔥 + 👥👥👥

were called. After the fire was put out all of the

people had 🧊 + CREAM .

What is a compound word? How many compound words are there in this story?

Write a rebus story of your own. Here are some words that may help you: *stoplight*, *horseshoe*, *tablespoon*, *catfish*, *kneecap*. You may think of others. Did you find that your rebus story took longer to write than other stories? Would you like to use rebus writing all of the time? Why or why not?

Invent a Name

When a new machine is invented, a new name has to be made for it. *Spacecraft* was the new name given to a machine that we now hear about every day. You can tell where the word *seaplane* came from. See if you can invent a new word for the machine that is carrying the boy.

What would you name a machine that can cut and paste at the same time?

What would you call a clock that calls out the time when you press a button?

Write all your new words on a piece of paper. Compare them with the words that others made up. Tell how you invented your words.

New Words to Read and Write

Read all the words in each list.

playful	scat	lift
helpful	score	drifted
hopeful	scale	shift
spoonful	scuff	draft
plateful	scold	softer

Read these suffixes.

ful   ly   er   est

When a suffix is added to a word, a syllable may be added. Try adding one of these suffixes to each word below. Then tell how many syllables the word has. Can you add more than one to the same word? Which words will not have one of these suffixes added to them?

fret	mouth	thank	fright
tight	hate	sick	live
joy	force	fond	black
dish	neighbor	slow	sweet
first	friend	paint	garden

Mom poured her coffee, piping hot, and she left it on the breakfast table. Mom often poured her coffee this way.

I drank my milk and ate my breakfast, but Mom's coffee stayed in the cup. She was fixing lunches for Dad and me. We were in a hurry.

My dad is a teacher. He teaches science, and sometimes we talk things over. But he won't answer some of my questions about science. He always says, "Guess and try."

196

Mom was a long time fixing the lunches. Dad grabbed his, and rushed off to teach his science class. Mom tasted her coffee and made a funny face.

"Too cold," she said. She threw it away and poured some hot coffee into her cup.

I picked up my lunch and walked to school. I had time to think, so I said to myself, "How come Mom's coffee got cold?"

But I didn't have time to guess and try to find out why hot coffee in a cup cooled off.

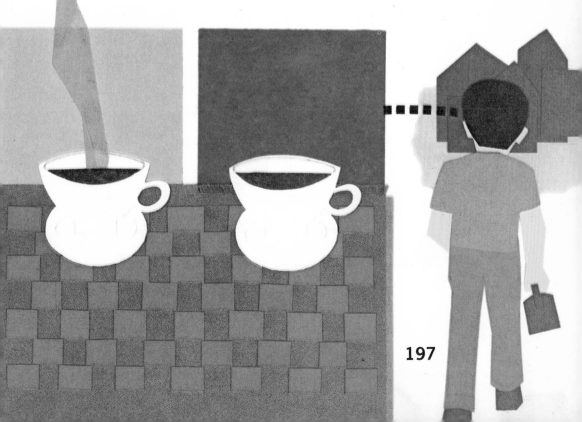

We eat our lunches out of doors at our school. Sometimes it gets hot out there. Sometimes Pedro Juarez sits near me. This day he did.

He likes milk. I do too. We buy cartons of milk for lunch at school. I like my milk good and cold. So I drink it right away.

Pedro pours his milk into a saucer, which he brings in his lunch pail every day. The milk sits in the saucer while Pedro eats. "I let my milk warm up," he always says.

Here was a funny thing! My mom poured hot coffee into a cup, and it cooled off. Pedro pours cold milk into a saucer, and it warms up. "What's going on around here?" I say to myself. "Has this anything to do with science?"

I talked to my dad about it after school.

"What's going on with the coffee and the milk?" I asked. "Anything to do with science?"

My dad winked. "Guess and try," he said.

So I did. Mom helped me pour some hot coffee into a cup. I poured some ice-cold milk into a saucer, myself. And then I waited.

I worked with Tricks, my Scotty dog. She goes to Obedience School and is learning to sit when I say, "Sit." It is hard work.

"How about that coffee and milk?" Dad called.

So I tried to find out. I put my finger into the coffee. It was not too hot, but it was not really cold.

I put my finger into the milk and swished it around in the saucer. I made small waves.

"How about it?" Dad called again.

"Oh," I said. "Funny thing. The milk isn't so cold now and the coffee isn't very hot. Each one is sort of cool."

My dad laughed. "Sort of?" he called.

"Well, the milk is cool," I called back. "The coffee feels warm, but it doesn't sting my finger."

Dad came out to look. He didn't try the coffee or the milk. He just said, "Maybe you have something here."

I wanted to be sure. So I dumped the coffee and the milk into the sink. Then I saw Dad looking at the cup and the saucer. It made me wonder. I looked at them too.

"Guess I'll try something new," I said.

"What?" Dad asked.

"Guess what," I said. I didn't want to tell him. So Dad had to wait too.

I asked Mom for some more hot coffee, but I didn't use the cup. Saucers were more fun. I took two saucers this time and poured cold milk into one of them. Mom poured the hot coffee into the other saucer.

"I am going to leave them here all night," I said.

Tricks went to bed and so did I. Sometimes Tricks sleeps in my room on her own blanket. This was one of those times. I always sleep harder when Tricks is snoring nearby. I guess she sleeps harder too.

We were the last ones up for breakfast.

Mom was making sandwiches. Dad was eating scrambled eggs. And my two saucers were sitting there on the kitchen table.

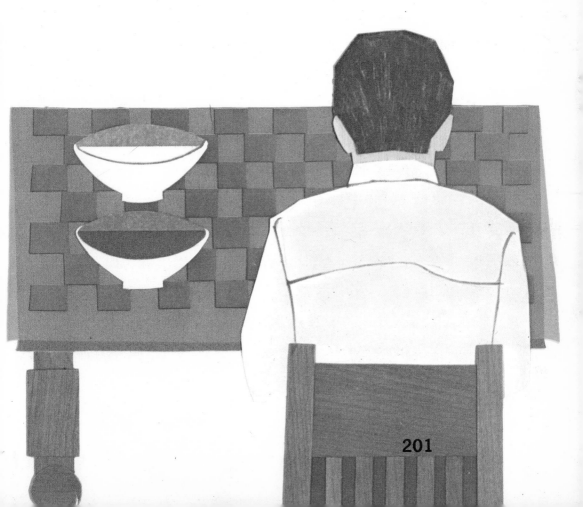

I put my finger into the milk and made small waves with it. It felt just right for swimming. I put a finger of my other hand into the saucer of coffee. At last I understood.

I looked at my Dad, and he was looking at me.

"It's something to do with science," I told him. "Guess and try."

And he said, "I did. That's how I know."

So now we two know the answer.

Do you?

Where Go the Boats?

Dark brown is the river,
Golden is the sand.
It flows along forever,
With trees on either hand.

Green leaves a-floating,
Castles of the foam,
Boats of mine a-boating—
Where will all come home?

On goes the river
And out past the mill,
Away down the valley,
Away down the hill.

Away down the river,
A hundred miles or more,
Other little children
Shall bring my boats ashore.

Robert Louis Stevenson

DIPPY'S DAY BY MOONLIGHT

It was evening on the desert. A full moon was rising. Dippy's day was just coming.

Desert sand in the daytime is too hot for a kangaroo rat like Dippy. He covers the openings of his house with dirt and sleeps in one room all day.

Night was daytime for Dippy. He woke up and stretched. He hopped around on his long hind legs to open the doors of his burrow.

That was easy! He just kicked aside little piles of dirt and let the moonlight come into the burrow.

204

Then he sat in a doorway on his hind legs and cleaned himself the way a cat does. He cleaned behind his ears. He smoothed his white front hairs and the tan fur on his back. He did not skip over his short front legs. When he finished, even the tuft of fur on his tail was fluffy and clean.

Breakfast came next. His little feet had made tiny tracks to nearby bushes. Dippy hopped off to them now. He sat up on his hind legs in front of some fat seeds and balanced himself with his long tail. With his front paws he brushed seeds from the stems into his open mouth.

A twig cracked close by! Dippy jumped ten feet. He changed his direction in midair. With zigzag leaps he reached the nearest hole into his burrow.

Inside he stopped, balanced himself, and trembled. His black eyes were wide open as he peeked out. A snake was going into the burrow of a neighbor rat, but Dippy was safe.

He stopped trembling and listened to other sounds. His ears spun around in different directions. Sand grains were blowing in the wind, and the full moon was higher. No snakes were near.

Dippy leaped to a spot of moonlight and froze again. Overhead an owl swished by, but it missed Dippy. Some other kangaroo rat might not be so lucky!

Dippy jumped to a clump of grasses. His front paws held some stems while his sharp teeth cut them off. He put them down to dry in a hollow of sand. He went from clump to clump, gathering his food and putting it to dry in the hollow.

It was hard work and his fur was full of dirt. He found a few seeds to eat, and then he headed for a bath in a dust hole.

It was just a hollow in the sand, but Dippy tested it well. There were tracks of birds and other animals all around it. There were some kangaroo-rat tracks too. This must be a favorite dust hole for a good bath.

Dippy hopped back to a nearby shadow. He looked and listened and waited. Nothing came to bother him, and into the dust hole he leaped.

He rolled around on his back in the hollow. He twisted and wiggled and turned. The dust was his bath water. It worked its way all through his fur and got rid of insects and twigs and dirt. It felt good !

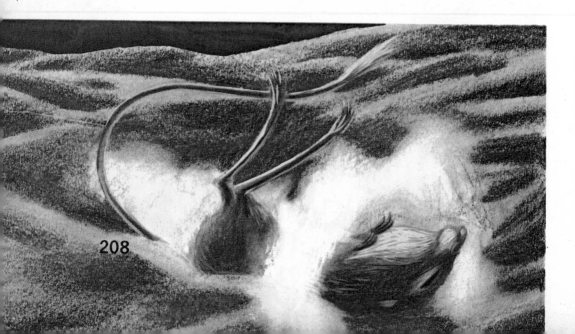

Dippy finished his bath and jumped back to the shadow to brush himself. His white and tan fur was soon smooth again. The tuft on the end of his tail was fluffy.

A twig snapped, and Dippy zigzagged with big hops to get away from some new danger. Trembling, he waited until the desert was quiet, and looked around with his bright black eyes.

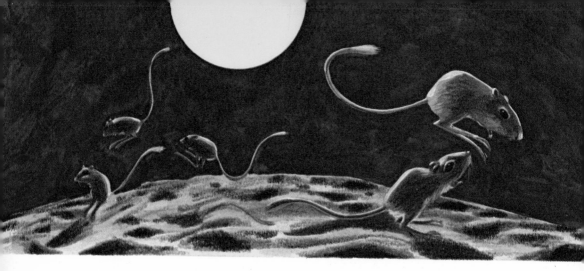

He saw kangaroo rats in the moonlight. They were playing tag and leapfrog on a sand hill, so he played with them.

All at once an owl hooted. Each rat leaped to his own burrow. A high scream told Dippy that one rat had not leaped fast enough.

A breeze carried the scent of ripe seeds to Dippy, and he was really hungry. He found some and ate a few. Then he filled his cheek pouches with some. His cheek pouches were fur-lined, a good basket for his seeds.

He carried them to a soft spot in the sand. He hid them in a little hollow and covered them. Back he went for more, always following the scent.

But another kangaroo rat was already stuffing his cheek pouches with seeds. Dippy leaped at him and landed, back to back, against the other rat. They kicked hard with their hind feet, and the sand flew in all directions. Each rat tried to keep his balance, but Dippy was bigger. One kick landed in the right spot. Over went the other rat. He rolled over and over, and Dippy chased him away.

Dippy went back to gather his seeds, but they were gone. Another rat had helped himself while Dippy was fighting.

His moonlight day was almost over, and he lost no time. He sat up on his hind legs and his nose twitched.

The right scent came, and he found more seeds. He ate some and then filled his cheek pouches. This time he took the seeds into his own burrow and stored them.

Daylight was coming. Dippy ate his supper and pushed dirt into each door of his burrow. He went into his sleeping room. He turned around and covered his nose with the fur tuft on his tail. One more wonderful day by moonlight was over, and it was bedtime for Dipodomys, the little kangaroo rat of the desert.

212

GOOD-NIGHT SONG

Good night ! good night ! the sun has set;
The slim, slow moon is hanging high;
And little flowers are dewy-wet
Where quiet shadows lie.
Each bird is sleepy in its nest;
Each baby lamb is safe from sight;
All the still world has gone to rest,
Good night ! good night !

The dusky stairway calls our feet,
The old clock gently bids us go,
Above, there wait us, cool and sweet,
Tiny white beds a-row.
One soft star at the window gleams,
Our little candle is alight,
Our eyelids droop with drowsy dreams—
Good night ! good night !

Nancy Byrd Turner

WHERE IS WATER?

Everyone knows the answer to that question. When rain falls, we see water in puddles. Sometimes water rushes down the side of a mountain, carrying rocks with it. In a quiet lake, water is like a mirror. You can see the sky reflected in it.

Water floats leaves and little sticks in a running river. Sometimes there is so much water that it floods the land. At the seashore great waves of water come in from the ocean. They rise in a tower of foam and fall back into the ocean again.

Sometimes water is not so easy to see. It is inside plants and animals. It is in all of us. Did you know that you are made mostly of water?

Water is almost everywhere. It spreads out when we spill it. It soaks into things. It may be flowing into a lake at one spot and quietly flowing out at another. It fills low places.

Water is liquid. It can be clean enough to drink or it can be full of mud and dirt. It can also be salty, as it is in the ocean.

Water will not burn. It can help to put out fires.

Wonderful, wonderful water!

Yes, it is a liquid. But is it always a liquid?

Doesn't running water change when cold, cold winter comes ? Is water always a liquid then ?

When it gets very cold, water has another form. It turns to ice. When ice is thick enough, you can run over it and skate on it.

Ice is water in its solid form. So is hail that pelts down in round, hard balls.

Glaciers and icebergs are water in this solid form. Have you ever seen a glacier ? Most glaciers are in high mountains. The ice in glaciers moves so slowly that you cannot see it move. But it does move. A mountain glacier is a solid river of snowy ice, that may move one inch in one day !

If the lower end of the glacier reaches the sea, great blocks of ice break off into the water. They are icebergs.

Snow is water in its solid form, because snow is made of delicate crystals of ice.

Where do snow crystals come from? And raindrops? And clouds? Where does the water they are made of come from? Do you ever wonder about that?

Here is one way to help you find out. Put a few drops of water in a saucer. Leave it there for a day or so. Then look at it again. The water is gone. It has gone into the air but you cannot see it there.

Lakes and oceans are like giant saucers that never dry up. So there must be lots of water in the air all the time.

Do you think this is where raindrops come from ? And snow ? And clouds ?

There is another way you may find out if water is really in the air. On a cold winter day, stand near a cold windowpane. Blow out a big breath of air against the glass. Do it again and again.

A foggy spot will come on the glass. Small drops of water will start to run down it. They were not there before you blew on the glass.

This form of water is in the air all the time. It was in your breath and you could not see it. Sneaky, isn't it ?

This is the third form of water. It is water vapor. Clouds and snow and raindrops all come from water vapor in the air.

Rain and snow and hail always fall. Rivers always run downhill. How does water get back up to make more rain and snow and hail ?

Do you ever wonder about that ?

SHADOWS ON THE MOON

What does the moon look like as it rides along in the sky? Do you ever play in the moonlight, and make shadows with your fingers? Do you ever play tag in the moonlight, and make shadows as you run?

Some people even find pictures in the moon and tell stories about them. Have you ever seen Moon-Boy in the moon? Some Indians in Alaska did. They were watching the moon, and they saw Moon-Boy. They were sure of it. They said that Moon-Boy spoke to the moon. They heard what he said. They told their children the story about it.

MOON-BOY[1]

At first, Moon-Boy lived on earth in a big family. He was a hunter. One day he came home late and hungry. But the food kettle was empty.

"There is nothing left to eat," his father said. When Moon-Boy began to cry, his father shouted, "Stop crying or I shall whip you!"

So the boy took the empty kettle and ran into the woods.

[1] Adapted from *The Moon Is a Crystal Ball,* by Natalia Belting, copyright 1952 by The Bobbs-Merrill Company, Inc., reprinted by permission of the publishers.

The night was clear. The moon was shining and full. Soon the Indians saw a strange shadow on the moon's face. Before that night it had always been clear, they said.

"It is the shadow of the boy," one Indian cried. "He is holding an empty kettle."

The boy was talking to the moon. They could hear his words.

"You, Moon," he said, "you are my father now. I will stay with you and have plenty to eat. My name is Sakesada. I am 'He-Who-Sits-On-The-Moon.'" And there he stayed.

He is very old now, the Indians say. He can no longer stand up straight. He is bent over halfway. You can see him there when the moon is shining and full.

Is Sakesada a shadow on the moon's face? Can you find a shadow there and tell a story about it?

It is fun to let your fingers dance and make shadows in the moonlight. It is fun to make up stories about the shadows on the moon.

The best fun is to find out why the moon has shadows, as it comes and goes in the sky.

Some day a spaceship may take you to the moon. You may really sit on it and take pictures of its mountains, or measure its big holes, called craters. Then you can zoom home to tell us what you found.

We do know some things to tell you before you go.

The moon is our nearest neighbor in space. It has flat places, high pointed mountains, and wide craters.

There is no air on the moon. There are no clouds, no wind, no rain. So there is no water. There are no rivers, no oceans.

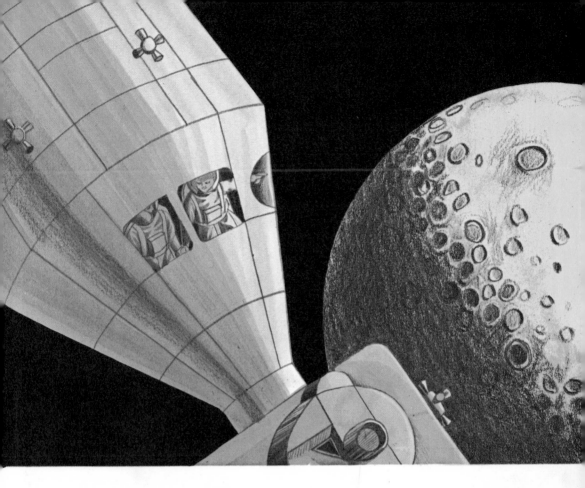

You will see stars in the daytime, if you go
to the moon. They will be clear bright points
of light, and the sky will be dark.

When we see the full moon rise in the sky,
it glows with light. The moon looks like a
shining silver ball, doesn't it? But the moon
has no light of its own.

Where does the shining light on the moon's face come from ? It comes from the sun and is reflected from the face of the moon.

Where there are mountains on the moon's face, the light makes shadows. They always point away from the sun.

Men of Science, called scientists, look at pictures of the moon's shadows and measure them.

These scientists can measure how high the mountains are by their shadows. When the mountains are very high, the shadows are long and shaped like ice-cream cones.

In these shadows the moon is colder than anything we know on the earth.

The pictures also show big craters on the moon. Scientists think that one of the craters may be 140 miles wide!

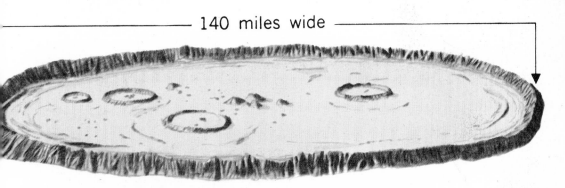

140 miles wide

Shadows tell us about the craters. They show that there are rings of mountains around these big holes. There are also mountains in the centers of some craters.

The moon shows us many "faces" as it rides along in the sky. It may be a thin crescent of light. It may look like a big letter D. The crescent, the letter D, and the full moon all reflect light from the sun.

Shadows have all kinds of stories to tell. There are old stories about Moon-Boy who lived on the moon. There are true stories which spacemen are telling nowadays. There will be new stories that you can tell *after* you take a trip to see the shadows on the moon.

Tic Tac Know

To play Tic Tac Know you will need a partner. Draw a Tic Tac Know frame like this ⊞ on a piece of paper or on the chalkboard. Make sure your spaces are large enough for the words. Write in the word-parts that you see here.

s	–at	–old	–eal
sc	–at	–old	–ared
scr	–atch	–oll	–eam

Here are the rules:

1. Decide who should go first.

2. The first player picks one of the sentence clues and reads it. Then he figures out the word that goes in the blank of the sentence clue. He does this by adding s, sc, or scr to one of the word parts in the Tic Tac Know frame until he finds the word that will fit his sentence clue.

   To help you, here is the answer for the first sentence clue: sat. Find the word–part at in the Tic Tac Know frame and write the s next to it. Remember not to use this sentence clue again.

230

3. The next player picks another sentence clue, tries to find the answer, and writes the letter or letters in the right space.

4. The winner is the player who can fill three spaces across, down, or diagonally with the right words.

Here are your sentence clues:

1. The tired old woman _____ down to rest.

2. Mother was angry but she did not _____ him.

3. The little boy made such a scene, that everyone could hear his _____.

4. A paper roll which we write on is called a _____.

5. Father _____ the house and we had to move.

6. She said, "_____" to make the cat go away.

7. She dropped the tray and made a long _____ on the new table.

8. The Halloween mask _____ the little boy.

9. The _____ balanced a ball on his nose.

Facts and Imagination

Long before people understood much about nature, they explained what happened by making up stories. Stories of this kind were called legends. One legend which you know tells about the Alaskan Indian boy named Sakesada who became He-Who-Sits-On-The-Moon.

Before scientists learned about the water cycle, people made up stories to explain such things as rain, fog, and snow. We know, also, that stories were told to explain why the sun crossed the sky.

Even though we know more about nature now, we still like to make up stories about how things came to be. Can you tell the difference between story writing and scientific writing?

Read the sentences below and decide which ones are facts and which might be used in an imaginary tale or legend.

1. The Sun was angry with the people on earth and shed many tears.
2. Ice and snow melt in the mountains and run into the rivers and streams.
3. The Fire God makes the snow turn to water to help things grow.
4. Water rises from oceans and changes into vapor and then falls to earth as rain.
5. Mr. Moon was smiling down at the boys and he was winking one eye.
6. Glaciers are masses of snow and ice.

MAGIC MAKERS

6

THE HANDRE

Once there was a handre. A handre is like a goblin, and this handre was very ugly. His great eyes rolled around. He had long sharp teeth and long sharp claws, which rattled. What he liked best was to jump out from behind a rock to frighten two certain little cats, who lived in a house down the road. He rolled his eyes, rattled his claws, and snarled at them. Then he vanished. The little cats would run home as fast as they could and hide in their beds.

234

One day the two little cats needed some butter and salt to put in their morning tea. "Let's go to the market," said one.

"What if we should meet the handre?" said the other.

They talked it over a while and decided that they would take a chance. "Maybe he has moved away," said one.

So off they went to market for butter and salt. On their way home, sure enough, out popped the handre from behind the rock, rolling his eyes. He rattled his claws and snarled.

Away they ran. But this time the handre didn't vanish. He followed them down the road. Whenever they peeked back, there he was, tapping his claws on the ground. How he laughed when the little cats scampered.

235

On they ran until they met a cow. "Where are you going so fast? On your way home from market, little cats?" asked the cow.

"The handre is chasing us," they gasped.

"I'll come with you," mooed the cow.

Next they met a dog, a crow, and a snake by the side of the path. "Why are you two cats and cow running so fast?" they asked.

"Because the handre is after us."

"We will help you," said the dog, the crow, and the snake. So they ran with the two little cats and the cow.

A little later they saw a pan of ashes, a box of needles, and a bowl of hard, dry peas. These things could talk, but they couldn't walk.

"You must be running away from the handre," said the peas.

"Yes," whispered the cats. "And the cow, the dog, and the crow, and the snake are going home with us."

"Well, if you will carry us, we can help too." So the two little cats picked up the ashes, the needles, and the peas. They put them inside their shirts so they wouldn't drop them.

The handre was getting closer and closer, and the two little cats could hear his claws rattle.

"Hurry, hurry, lock the door," the cats cried.

Quickly the cow stood by the stairs. The dog got behind the door. The crow hid in the water barrel, and the snake curled up behind the bread. The two little cats put the pan of ashes above the door. They put the needles in the bed, and the peas rolled down the steps. The little cats put a blanket over their heads.

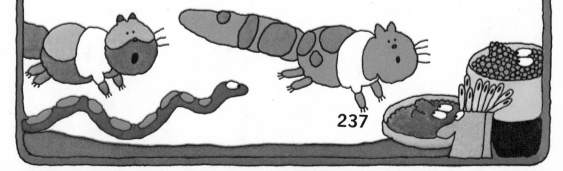

Sure enough, here came the handre. He found the door locked, so he just hopped in the window.

He rolled his eyes and rattled his claws and snarled. "Now I will really frighten those two little cats. Where are they?"

He went to get a drink from the water barrel, and the crow pecked him. He tried to eat the bread, and the snake hissed at him. He went upstairs. He got under a blanket in the bed and the needles prickled. He looked up on top of the door, and the ashes sprinkled in his eyes.

As the handre started down the stairs, the hard peas rolled under his feet, and he fell on the hard horns of the cow. The cow tossed him lightly to the dog, who opened his mouth to bite him.

By that time the handre was frightened out of his rattles and snarls and had vanished completely. When the dog snapped his jaws, there was nothing there.

Finally the two little cats came out from under the blanket and thanked each of their friends for chasing away the handre. They all sat down and had some hot buttered tea, and they never, never saw the handre again.

The Donkey Egg

The Hodja lived in a small village with his wife, Fatima. They had one little donkey, and how they wished for one more donkey!

The Hodja had a friend, Ali. At times they had quarrels. Then they were not such good friends for a while. One day Ali brought a strange gift to the Hodja. From the folds of his loose coat, he brought it forth. It was large and smooth and round.

He offered the gift to the Hodja and Fatima. "A donkey egg," Ali said. "You must sit on this egg for three weeks. Then a baby donkey will hatch from it. He will grow and grow. In a few months, you will have another sturdy donkey. He can carry your loads to market. He can carry you where you want to go."

The Hodja was surprised. Just a week ago he and Ali had almost had a bad quarrel. Now his friend was helping them to have a second donkey.

"We thank you up to the heavens," the Hodja cried.

"And seven times above the heavens!" Fatima cried.

They kissed Ali's hand and pressed it to their foreheads. Over and over they thanked him.

The next three weeks were long ones. While the Hodja sat on the donkey egg, Fatima was busy. She fixed the meals, and cleaned the house, and twirled her spindle, and visited with the neighbor women.

While Fatima sat on the donkey egg, the Hodja went to market, and chopped wood, and talked with his friends in the coffee house.

Sitting on the donkey egg, the Hodja smoked his water pipe. He thought of wise advice to give his friends. He dreamed about the donkey.

Sitting on the donkey egg, Fatima twirled her hand spindle. She spun pounds and pounds of wool into scratchy yarn.

The neighbors came in to talk. The men came when the Hodja was sitting on the egg. The women came when they knew it was Fatima's turn to sit on it.

"Let us see the donkey egg," the women said. "We have never seen one."

"Oh, no," Fatima would reply. "We cannot let the egg get cold. We cannot take any chances." And so, no one but the Hodja and Fatima ever saw it.

242

A market day passed. A bath day passed. The first week was gone. The men went to the coffee house a second time. The people went to the public bath house a second time. And another week was gone. Then another market day and another bath day went by. Fatima had twirled her hand spindle for many hours. The third week was over.

At last it was time for the baby donkey to come out of the donkey egg. The Hodja tapped it. It was very soft. "Ah, yes," he said, "soon it will hatch."

So the Hodja and his wife took turns sitting on the donkey egg again. They sat for one more market day, and one more day at the public bath house. The egg grew even softer. But no baby donkey came out of it.

243

The egg did have a strange odor. It grew stronger as the egg grew softer. At last, the Hodja said to Fatima, "This egg is rotten. We cannot hope for our baby donkey any more."

He picked up the old donkey egg and put it under his arm. He walked slowly to the marketplace. All the people turned to look at him.

When his friends saw the egg, they nodded and smiled. The women looked at each other behind their veils. Then they looked at the Hodja and shook their heads. How strange everyone acted. The Hodja did not know why.

Children began to follow him. They were singing a silly chant. "*Donkey eggs grow on pumpkin vines,*" they chanted. They chanted it over and over. The Hodja was too sad to listen to the words. He went out of the town and climbed a hill.

At the top of the hill he stopped. He put the pumpkin on the ground. To the Hodja, the pumpkin was still a donkey egg. It started rolling down the hillside.

It rolled over rocks and around bushes. It rolled against a tree. It hit a stone and cracked open.

Under that tree a long-eared rabbit was sleeping. When the pumpkin burst open, the rabbit jumped up. He hopped off down the hill and out of sight.

It was a beautiful long-eared rabbit. The Hodja saw him. "Oh," he groaned. "The baby donkey at last! The donkey egg was just ready to hatch. *May heaven help us all,*" he shouted. "Now it has hatched and our baby donkey is lost forever!"

The Three Spinning Fairies

Characters

ARDIS	THICKTHUMB
STEPMOTHER	GREATLIP
QUEEN	PRINCE
BROADFOOT	KING

SEVERAL WEDDING GUESTS

Act One

(*The inside of a small cottage.* ARDIS *sits before a small spinning wheel. Her* STEPMOTHER *paces about.*)

STEPMOTHER: No more excuses, you lazy girl! Get on with your spinning!

ARDIS: Dear Stepmother, please give me another task. May I milk the cow?

STEPMOTHER: You've already milked her. Have you forgotten? Now get on with your spinning!

ARDIS: The floor then, dear Stepmother. Let me wash the floor.

STEPMOTHER: Excuses! More excuses! You've scrubbed the floor twice already today. If you've forgotten, look about you. Now get spinning, you lazy girl!

(**ARDIS** *tries to spin, but the yarn tangles.*)

ARDIS: Oh, dear Stepmother, I've forgotten how to turn the wheel. Please may I do some baking—or some mending?

STEPMOTHER: You've already baked bread enough to last a week, and you've mended everything in sight! Now spin, you lazy thing, and get on with it!

ARDIS: Perhaps, dear Stepmother, if you would show me how—

STEPMOTHER (*grabbing a broom*): Show you! I'll show you! Lazy! Good-for-nothing!

(**ARDIS** *screams and dashes around the room, trying to keep away from the broom, as the* **QUEEN** *enters the room. When the* **STEPMOTHER** *sees the* **QUEEN**, *she drops the broom and stares.*)

QUEEN: My good woman, what is going on here? I heard screaming from the road as I drove past in my carriage.

STEPMOTHER: Oh, Your Majesty, it is my stepdaughter. She—she sits at that spinning wheel from dawn till dark. I am a poor woman, Your Majesty. I cannot afford to keep buying flax, and yet she will not stop spinning!

QUEEN: Good woman, let me take your daughter to the castle. I have enough flax, and she can spin as long as she likes.

STEPMOTHER: As you wish, Your Majesty, but I won't be surprised if you are soon as angry with her as I.

QUEEN: Nonsense! I am never happier than when I hear the sound of spinning. Come along, my girl.

Act Two

(A room in the castle with a spinning wheel in the center and with bundles of flax piled everywhere. The QUEEN *enters the room, leading* ARDIS.*)*

QUEEN: Here you are, my dear. Next door to this room are two more rooms just like it. Spin all this flax, and you shall have my son, the Prince, for your husband.

ARDIS: Your Majesty, I am only a poor girl, and—

QUEEN: My son has no need to marry a rich girl. A clever girl—that's the kind of wife he must have. Now I know you are happy to spend your time doing what you love best, so I will leave you and come back tomorrow.

*(*QUEEN *leaves.* ARDIS *paces about.)*

250

ARDIS: What shall I do? I've tried and tried, but I've just never been able to learn to spin.

(*ARDIS sits at the spinning wheel, but soon the flax is a huge tangle.*)

ARDIS: Oh, it is hopeless! The Queen will surely think I am lazy. What can I do!

(*ARDIS begins to cry.* **BROADFOOT**, **THICKTHUMB**, *and* **GREATLIP** *enter.* **BROADFOOT** *has one very large foot.* **THICKTHUMB** *has one thumb as large as a man's hand.* **GREATLIP'S** *lower lip sticks out several inches past her nose.*)

251

BROADFOOT: There, there, Ardis. Do not weep.

ARDIS: Who are you? And how do you know my name?

BROADFOOT: I am Broadfoot, and these are my sisters, Thickthumb, and Greatlip. We know many things, and we have come to help you.

GREATLIP: Yes, to help you.

ARDIS: You are very kind, but I am afraid no one can help me. Why, I could never spin this flax in a hundred years, even if I knew how to spin.

THICKTHUMB: That is why we are here.

BROADFOOT: We can spin this flax into yarn before morning.

THICKTHUMB: And we'll be glad to do it. We love to spin.

GREATLIP: Yes, we love to spin!

ARDIS: But how could I ever repay you?

THICKTHUMB: We ask no pay. Just invite us to the wedding, so that we may share your joy.

BROADFOOT: And at the wedding, so that we may sit by you at the family table, you must introduce us as your cousins.

ARDIS: Oh, I'll gladly invite you to the wedding. And you are so kind I truly wish you were my cousins.

THICKTHUMB: Very well, then. Let's get on with our spinning.

GREATLIP: Yes, on with our spinning!

253

Act Three

(The same room very early the next morning. Yarn now fills the whole room. BROADFOOT and THICKTHUMB and GREATLIP stand looking at the yarn. ARDIS stares and stares.)

ARDIS: I can hardly believe it. To think that all three rooms are done!

BROADFOOT: Well, we are finished. Soon the Queen will return, so we must be going.

GREATLIP: Yes, we must be going!

ARDIS: Oh, my dear friends, I can never thank you.

THICKTHUMB: No need to thank us, Ardis. Just be a good wife to the Prince, and don't forget your promise.

GREATLIP: Yes, don't forget your promise!

(BROADFOOT, GREATLIP, and THICKTHUMB exit. Then the QUEEN enters and stares about her.)

QUEEN: I can't believe my eyes! Come, we will get you some food, and then you must rest before you begin on the other two rooms.

ARDIS: Thank you, Your Majesty, but the flax in all three rooms is spun.

QUEEN: I am at a loss for words!

ARDIS: I am happy if you are pleased, Your Majesty.

QUEEN: My dear, I am overjoyed! You are, indeed, a clever girl and the wife for the Prince. Come, we will announce the coming wedding throughout the Kingdom.

ARDIS: May I ask one favor, Your Majesty?

QUEEN: Of course. Anything you wish!

ARDIS: I have three dear cousins who have been very kind to me in the past. May I invite them to the wedding?

QUEEN: You may invite anyone you wish. Now come. There is much to be done this happy day.

Act Four

(*The great hall of the castle.* ARDIS *and the* PRINCE *stand arm in arm. The* KING *and* QUEEN *greet guests who enter and leave.* BROADFOOT, THICKTHUMB, *and* GREATLIP *enter. Everyone turns to stare but* ARDIS, *who rushes to greet them. The* PRINCE *follows, staring.*)

ARDIS: Dear cousins, I am so glad you could come!

BROADFOOT: How beautiful you look, my dear, and how happy.

THICKTHUMB: Now pay no attention to us, Ardis. We'll just mingle and enjoy ourselves. It was kind of you to invite us.

GREATLIP: Yes, it was kind of you to invite us!

(*The Three go to greet the* KING *and* QUEEN. *The* PRINCE *leads* ARDIS *to one side, away from the others.*)

256

PRINCE: Those three women—did you say they were your cousins?

ARDIS: Yes, and three more wonderful cousins I could never hope to have!

PRINCE: I'm sure they are very nice. Still, it does seem odd.

ARDIS: Odd? I don't understand.

PRINCE: I mean, my dear, that you are so beautiful, and to be quite truthful, I have never seen three more ugly-looking women.

ARDIS: I'm happy that you think me beautiful, dear Husband. And I'm sure that when you get to know my cousins, you will have forgotten their strange looks.

(**KING** *and* **QUEEN** *approach and lead* **ARDIS** *away as the* **KING** *speaks.*)

KING. Come, my dear. You must meet more of the guests.

(*The* **PRINCE** *walks about from one fairy to another, staring. They do not seem to notice. At last he leads* **BROADFOOT** *to the front of the stage.*)

PRINCE: Pardon me, Cousin, but I cannot help staring at your foot.

BROADFOOT: Oh, many people stare at my foot. It is very broad.

PRINCE: I hope you won't mind if I ask how it came to be so.

BROADFOOT: Not at all, Your Highness. Once my foot was as slim as that of my cousin, Ardis. Everyone in our family loves to spin, you know. And when one spins, one turns the wheel.

PRINCE: You turn the wheel with your foot?

BROADFOOT: Oh, yes! I can turn the wheel faster than anyone in the family.

PRINCE: I see. Yes, I see.

(*The* PRINCE *leaves* BROADFOOT *and brings* THICKTHUMB *to the front of the stage.*)

PRINCE: Excuse me, Cousin, but I cannot help staring at your thumb.

THICKTHUMB: Oh I am quite used to it. After all, not many have such a thumb.

PRINCE: I hope you won't mind my asking how it came to be so.

THICKTHUMB: I am happy to tell you, Your Highness. Once my thumb was quite ordinary—much like that of Ardis, your lovely bride. Our family, you know, is known for its spinners, and with this thumb I twist thread faster than anyone.

PRINCE: Twisting the thread made your thumb thick ?

THICKTHUMB: Yes, and now I have a thumb that is really something !

PRINCE: Yes. Yes, indeed !

(**PRINCE** *leaves* **THICKTHUMB** *and brings* **GREATLIP** *to the front of the stage.*)

PRINCE: I hope, dear Cousin, that you won't think me rude, but it is hard not to notice your unusual lower lip.

GREATLIP: Yes, I have an unusual lower lip !

PRINCE: Tell me, has spinning made it so ?

GREATLIP: Yes, spinning has made it so. I moisten the thread ! I moisten the thread !

(*The* **PRINCE** *leaves* **GREATLIP** *and goes to* **ARDIS.**)

PRINCE: My dear, I have something to ask of you.

ARDIS: How can I refuse my husband anything on our wedding day?

PRINCE: I have talked to your cousins, and I know how much spinning means to your family. Still, it is my wish that my beautiful wife not touch a spinning wheel again! Can you bear to give up spinning, my dear?

ARDIS (*smiling at the Three, and then turning back to the* **PRINCE**): For your sake, my love, I will do just that!

Make Your Own Story

Now that you know more about folk tales, here are some characters for your very own tale.

King Bong is a wicked man. He is greedy and selfish. Yet he wants the people in his kingdom to like him.

Princess Rose, King Bong's daughter, is very sad. She likes the people in the kingdom and helps them whenever she can. The people like her very much.

Wug is the son of the village shoemaker. He helps his father in the shop and often runs errands to the castle.

Remember the way in which the story of "The Three Spinning Fairies" was told. The fairies helped Ardis with her problem. Thinking about how that story begins and ends may help you use the three new characters in telling your own folk tale.

What's a Folk Tale ?

Storytelling is fun. Many, many years ago, when there were no television sets, movies, or books, even before men knew how to write, people loved to tell stories to each other. Grandparents told stories to parents. Parents told the same stories to their children. When the children grew up, they told the same stories to their children. And so it went, for many, many years, until these stories were finally written down. Many of these old stories are called folk tales.

Look at the pictures below. They are clues to some very old folk tales. Can you name the story ?

What is alike about all these tales ?
Which ones might have really happened ?
Which ones have magic in them ?
Is there something exciting in each one ?
Who are the unpleasant characters ?
What problem does the main character have ?
How does each story end ?

What's in the Train?

The train which you see below has just come through a sandstorm in the desert. Some of the letters which tell what the freight cars carry have been worn off by the sand and the wind.

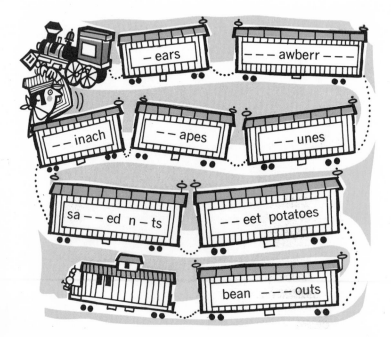

Can you help the engineer find out what is in each car? Two clues will help you. First, all of the freight cars contain food. Second, the missing letters are: *p*, *pr*, *sp*, *spr*, *str*, *sw*, *gr*, *u*, *ies*, and *lt*.
Write the words on paper.

Charlie the Tramp [1]

by RUSSELL HOBAN   Pictures by LILLIAN HOBAN

"Well, well," said Grandfather Beaver one day when he came to visit, "Charlie is getting to be a big boy."

"Yes, he is," said Father. "He is coming right along."

Grandfather smiled at Charlie and took a quarter out of his vest pocket.

"What are you going to be when you grow up, Charlie?" asked Grandfather.

"I am going to be a tramp," said Charlie.

"A tramp!" said Mother.

"A tramp!" said Father.

"A tramp!" said Grandfather, and he put the quarter back in his vest pocket.

"Yes," said Charlie, "I am going to be a tramp."

"I am surprised to hear that," said Father. "Your grandfather has been doing beaver work for many years, and I too am a beaver, but you want to be a tramp."

"That is how it is now-a-days," said Grandfather, shaking his head. "When I was young, children did not want to be tramps."

"I don't think Charlie really wants to be
a tramp," said Mother.

"Yes, I do," said Charlie. "Tramps don't
have to learn how to chop down trees and
how to roll logs and how to build dams.

"Tramps don't have to practice swimming and diving and holding their breath under water.

"Nobody looks to see if their teeth are sharp. Nobody looks to see if their fur is oiled.

"Tramps carry sticks with little bundles tied to them. They sleep in a field when the weather is nice, and when it rains they sleep in a barn.

"Tramps just tramp around and have a good time. And when they want something to eat, they do little jobs for anybody that wants little jobs done."

"I have lots of little jobs for you to do,"
said Father. "You can help me cut saplings
for our winter food. You can help me dig
extra tunnels for our lodge. And of course
the dam always needs repairs."

"That is not little jobs," said Charlie. "That's hard work."

"When I was young," said Grandfather, "children did hard work. Now-a-days all they want to do is little jobs."

"Well," said Father, "if Charlie wants to be a tramp, then I think he should be a tramp. I think we should not stand in his way."

"The weather is nice and warm now,"
said Charlie. "May I start sleeping in
fields?"

"All right," said Mother.

Charlie tied up some fig newtons and some Good-and-Plenties in a handkerchief. Then he tied the handkerchief to a stick and he was ready to go.

"Now it is time for me to be on the road and away," said Charlie.

"Good-bye, Mr. Tramp," said Father and Grandfather.

"Good-bye, Mr. Tramp," said Mother. "Come home in time for breakfast, and don't forget to brush your teeth tonight."

"Good-bye," said Charlie. "Tramps don't brush their teeth."

He got into his little boat, rowed across the pond, and tramped off down the road, while Mother and Father and Grandfather waved to him.

"Now that I think of it," said Grandfather, "I wanted to be a tramp when I was little, just like Charlie."

"So did I," said Father.

"That is how men are," said Mother. "They all want to be tramps."

Charlie tramped down the road, kicking a stone and whistling a tramping song as he went.

He looked at the blue hills far away, and he listened to cowbells tinkling in distant meadows.

Sometimes he stopped to throw stones at telephone poles, and sometimes he sat under a tree and watched the clouds roll by.

Charlie kept tramping until it was almost sundown, and then he picked a field to sleep in. He picked a field where daisies grew, and the grass and the clover smelled sweet.

Charlie untied his little bundle and took out some fig newtons and some Good-and-Plenties, and he ate them while the stars came out.

"Being a tramp is nice," said Charlie to himself, and he went to sleep.

Mother was watching for him at the window the next morning when he rowed across the pond.

"Here comes Charlie," she said to Father, "with his fur every which way and a bundle of daisies on his stick."

"Good morning, Lady," said Charlie when Mother opened the door. And he gave her the daisies. "Do you have a little job I can do for my breakfast?" he said.

"You can bail out the big rowboat," said Father. "That will be a nice little job for you."

"All right," said Charlie. "And then I will eat my breakfast on the back steps, because that is how we tramps do it."

So Charlie bailed out the rowboat. And while he was eating his breakfast on the back steps, Father came and sat down beside him. "How do you like being a tramp?" he said.

"I like it fine," said Charlie. "It is a lot easier than being a beaver."

"How did you sleep last night?" said Father.

"Fine," said Charlie. "But something kept waking me up."

"Was it anything scary?" said Father.

"No," said Charlie, "it was something nice, but I don't know what it was. I will have to listen for it again tonight."

Then Charlie rowed across the pond and went off down the road, whistling his tramping song.

Charlie tramped all day.

He listened to the birds singing.
He smelled the flowers that grew by the side
of the road. Sometimes he stopped to pick
blackberries. Sometimes he walked along the
top rails of fences.

At lunch time and dinner time Charlie went home and did little jobs for his lunch and his dinner.

He stacked winter saplings in the basement for his lunch. And for his dinner he helped his father fix a broken plank in the boat landing.

After dinner, Charlie went back to the field where the clover and the daisies grew. Charlie ate his fig newtons and his Good-and-Plenties, and he listened for the sound he had heard the night before.

Charlie heard the frogs and the crickets singing in the quiet of the night, and he heard something else. He heard a trickling, tickling kind of a little song that had no words.

The trickling, tickling song made Charlie want to hear it better. So he got up and went down to the trees where the sound was coming from.

He saw a little stream that sang as it ran in the moonlight, and he sat down and listened to the song again. But the sound of the trickling kept tickling Charlie, and he could not sit still.

So he took off his clothes, and he dived
into the stream and swam around inside the
song the water was singing.

Then Charlie climbed out and cut down a
little tree that was growing on the bank.
When the tree fell down, he rolled it into the
water.

Charlie took a deep breath and swam to
the bottom of the stream with the tree and
stuck it in the mud so that it would not
float away.

Then he listened to the song of the water, and he liked it better than he had before. So Charlie cut down some more trees, and he began to make a little dam to keep all

the water from trickling away.

Charlie worked on his dam all night. And by morning the stream had widened into a pond. Then the song of the water stopped tickling Charlie, and he said, "Now I guess I can go back to sleep."

So he brushed his teeth to keep them sharp. He oiled his fur to keep it waterproof. And he went to sleep in an old hollow tree by his new pond.

Charlie slept right through breakfast time, and Mother began to worry when she did not see him.

"I am sure Charlie is all right," said Father, "but I think we should look for him anyhow." And he went down to the boat landing and slapped the water with his tail, WHACK!

WHACK! answered Grandfather with his tail, and he came over to see what was the matter.

"I never did think any good would come of letting that boy run off to be a tramp," said Mother.

"That's how it is now-a-days," said Grandfather. "Boys run off, and no good comes of it."

So Mother and Father and Grandfather went looking for Charlie, and after a while they came to the new pond. But they did not see Charlie sleeping in the hollow tree.

"I don't remember seeing a pond around
here before," said Grandfather.

"Neither do I," said Father. "It must be
a new one."

"That's a pretty good pond," said Grandfather. "I wonder who made it?"

"I don't know," said Father. "You think maybe Harry Beaver might have done it?"

"No," said Grandfather. "Harry always makes a sloppy dam, and this one's not sloppy at all."

"What about old Zeb Beaver?" said Father. "Zeb always makes a good-looking dam."

"No," said Grandfather. "Zeb never makes a round pond like this one. Zeb always likes a long-shaped pond."

"You're right," said Father. "He does."

"You know," said Mother to Father, "this pond looks like the ponds you make."

"She's right," said Grandfather. "It does."

"That's funny," said Father. "I didn't make it. I wonder who did?"

"I did," said Charlie, waking up and coming out of the hollow tree. "That's my pond."

"That's your pond?" said Father.

"That's my pond," said Charlie.

"I thought you were a tramp," said Grandfather. "Tramps don't make ponds."

"Well," said Charlie, "sometimes I like to tramp around, and sometimes I like to make ponds."

"Any tramp that can make a pond like that is going to be some beaver one of these days," said Father.

"That's how it is now-a-days," said
Grandfather. "You never know when a tramp
will turn out to be a beaver." And he took
the quarter out of his vest pocket and gave
it to Charlie.

"Thank you," said Charlie. "Where's
Mother?"

But Mother had run back to the boat, rowed across the pond as fast as she could, and had flapjacks and maple syrup ready on the table when the men got home.

• New Words in This Book •

The following new words are presented in *How It Is Nowadays*, Level Eight, Reading 360. Words printed in regular type are new basic words. Those underlined are enrichment words.

The decodable words in this book, because of the large number, are not listed here. Decodable words occurring in the selections are listed at the beginning of each lesson plan in the Teachers' Edition of Level Eight.

11	Kukui	17	trying	32	lifted
	mynah	18	cried		great
	island	19	desperation		believe
	Maui		advice		Hilda
12	mimic	20	brought		Heron
	mistress		bewildered	35	Rachel
13	pussy	21	worse	36	flying
	sweet		terrible		goodness
	kept	24	cackledecackle	40	William
	sure	26	wonderful		August
15	begun	28	senses		watermelon
	behind	29	Flossie		gifts
	preened		Flamingo	41	breath
	pointed		flew		Julie
	toward		Florida	42	interrupted
	hele		spend		agreed
	pēlā		huge		suggested
	shadows	30	Olive		sighed
	mongoose		rocket	43	busy
16	suddenly		silo		true
	mai	31	noticed		whole

300

303

241	heavens			Majesty	254	exit
	twirled			stepdaughter	255	loss
	spindle			afford		overjoyed
242	scratchy	249	daughter		announce
	reply		castle		Kingdom
243	public		nonsense	256	attention
244	odor		happier		mingle
	rotten	250	bundles		ourselves
	veils		husband	257	truthful
	pumpkin	251	able	258	approach
246	Ardis		tangle		Highness
	several		hopeless	259	ordinary
	guests	252	hundred	260	rude
	cottage	253	repay		unusual
	excuses		introduce		moisten
247	twice		cousins	261	refuse
248	carriage	254	return		

D E F G H I J   7 6 5 4 3 2 1   PRINTED IN THE U.S.A.